W9-CBA-416

QUANTITY AND QUALITY

QUANTITY AND QUALITY

The Hayden Colloquium on Scientific Method and Concept

EDITED BY

DANIEL LERNER

CONTRIBUTORS

John G. Kemeny
Harold D. Lasswell
Wassily Leontief
Daniel Lerner
Walter A. Rosenblith
Joseph J. Spengler
S. S. Stevens
Victor F. Weisskopf

THE FREE PRESS OF GLENCOE, INC.
A DIVISION OF THE CROWELL-COLLIER PUBLISHING COMPANY

Printed in the United States of America

For information, address:

The Free Press of Glencoe, Inc.
A DIVISION OF THE CROWELL-COLLIER PUBLISHING COMPANY
60 Fifth Avenue, New York 11

Library of Congress Catalog Card Number: 60–15869

The essays of Professors Kemeny, Lasswell, Leontief, and Weisskopf originated in the Hayden Colloquium of the Massachusetts Institute of Technology. They and the paper by Professor Stevens were first published in *Dædalus*, the Journal of the American Academy of Arts and Sciences.

PREFACE

THE HAYDEN COLLOQUIUM of the Massachusetts Institute of Technology is a distinguished lecture series concerned with common problems of concept and method in the diverse fields of modern knowledge. Each year the Colloquium selects a classic theme which has preoccupied thinkers over many generations, sometimes over centuries. The lecturers are asked to clarify the meaning of this classic theme for contemporary work in their own field of knowledge. How are the problems historically associated with this theme encountered by living people concerned with theory, research, and judgment in fields ranging from aesthetics to zoology? How have new versions of the old problems been set and met? To what extent is the traditional formulation of these problems no longer relevant to contemporary needs? In instances in which the contemporary formulation is more amenable to current thinking, but is so stated as to leave the older problem unsolved, what importance has the unsolved residue?

To questions such as these our lecturers respond in terms of work in progress, and their responses are critically discussed by the members of the Colloquium. This practice has produced, over the years, a continuing conversation among the various fields of knowledge and common problems of considerable breadth and depth have emerged. It has appeared worth while to preserve the final form of these lectures in book form. Our first Colloquium was published by The Free Press as *Evidence and Inference.* The second Colloquium is here presented in the same format as *Quantity and Quality.* The third Colloquium, recently concluded, will be published in due course as *Parts and Wholes.*

The making of such a book represents the cooperative work of many hands. The lecture series has been sponsored by the M.I.T. School of Humanities and Social Studies, from funds granted by the Carnegie Corporation of New York. Dean John E. Burchard made the Colloquium possible and has been a firm supporter of its continuance. Thanks are due to the American Academy of Arts and Sciences, and particularly to its general editor, Dr. Gerald Holton. Through his cooperation the papers by John G. Kemeny, Victor F. Weisskopf, S. S. Stevens, Wassily Leontief, and Harold D. Lasswell first appeared in a special issue of *Daedalus* (Fall, 1959). The paper by Walter A. Rosenblith, who originally delivered his lecture in the "Evidence and Inference" series, was especially adapted for this volume from his current work in neurophysiology. We are indebted to J. J. Spengler for permitting us to include his paper, which, although prepared for another occasion, provides a clarifying historical complement to the original set of contributions.

Thanks are due to Morton Gorden, Dorothy Dorman, and, as always, to Jean Lerner for their aid in the complex process of transforming spoken words into print.

Daniel Lerner

CONTENTS

QUANTITY AND QUALITY

INTRODUCTION

On Quantity and Quality

Daniel Lerner

"It is quality rather than quantity that matters" (*Epistles*, 45:1). This simple utterance has resounded through the centuries. Quality signified, in this usage, the "nature" and "essence" of matters—hence, the true goal of knowledge. Compared with the dignity of understanding the essential nature of things, efforts to describe the actual behavior of things seemed trivial and even degrading to many philosophers. To substitute for the question, "what kind?" the apparently superficial question, "how much?"—with its ambition of predicting recurrent events—seemed even impious to thinkers who regarded the natural order as divine and inscrutable. St. Augustine enjoined good Christians to "beware of mathematicians and all those who make empty prophecies."[1] And Edmund Burke, centuries later, as the period of Enlightenment passed into the era of science, protested: "The Age of Chivalry is gone. That of sophists, economists, and *calculators* has succeeded and the glory of Europe is extinguished for ever."[2]

This protest was uttered at the start of the nineteenth century, when confidence in metrical methods was moving toward an apogee. Quantity emerged as the key symbol in the new conception of science. Not only the physical universe, from atoms to planets, but also human behavior, from individual sensation to economic systems, was subjected to measurement. Even the full array of social sciences was pervaded by quantification. In England, particularly, and especially in economics, following elaboration of the neoclassic model of the market economy, quantity became omnipotent. W. Stanley Jevons said flatly: "I contend that all economic writers must be mathematical so far as they are scientific at all, because they treat of economic quantities, and the relations of such quantities, and all quantities and relations of quantities come within the scope of mathematics."[3]

The Nineteenth Century and After

At the end of the nineteenth century, when quantification had already produced a succession of scientific triumphs, the great innovations stimulated by the mathematization of physics had spread euphoric confidence in pure mathematics as the root of all knowledge. Its power was demonstrated by the continuous discovery of new uses, both theoretical and practical, for its abstract relationships. Professor Dantzig has cited some vivid examples of the powerful interaction between mathematics and the physical sciences in the nineteenth century and after:

> The conic sections, invented in an attempt to solve the problem of doubling the altar of an oracle, ended by becoming the orbits followed by the planets in their courses about the sun. The imaginary magnitudes invented by Cardan and Bombelli describe in some strange way characteristic features of alternating currents. The absolute differential calculus, which originated as a fantasy of Riemann, became the mathematical vehicle for the theory of Relativity. And the matrices which were a complete abstraction in the days of Cayley and Sylvester appear admirably adapted to the exotic situation exhibited by the quantum theory of the atom.[4]

The social sciences also made striking progress through mathematization and quantification in these decades (which Kurt Lewin has called their "Galilean period"). The earliest work of John Graunt on mortality and its laws, as Professor Spengler's essay tells us, "made possible a theory of annuities, of great importance when tontines and annuities were used as forms of public debt; it also contributed, along with probability theory, to the establishment of insurance." Further work on "the chances of death" enabled Galton and Pearson to strengthen the new science of genetics by mathematical analysis of its statistical derivations.

A high point was reached when Karl Pearson, working under a long-term grant from the Worshipful Company of Drapers on the vulgar problem of standardizing body measurements, developed the product-moment correlation coefficient. This intellectual breakthrough occurred in the context of institutional innovation:

My object during the past forty years has been to build up a laboratory unique of its kind, a place where a novel calculus should be applied to problems concerning living forms. This purpose involved the development of a new form of mathematical analysis, which has grown largely through the work of my pupils scattered through the world, or through those studying their writings. It will continue to grow, but will only grow with due sense of proportion, *if in touch with practical needs,* and if it develops in association with anthropometry, medicine, biometry, and the sciences of heredity and psychology. That is to say, if our new calculus is not to become a field for the exploits of the pure mathematician, it must be linked with investigations into topics where its aid is most needed; it must remain a practical science, i.e. *applied* statistics. . . . Such a laboratory would have seemed a vain dream forty years ago, but we have gone a long way towards it since.[5]

Pearson's new laboratory proposed nothing less than to institutionalize the scientific solution of societal problems through quantification (the "novel calculus"). This, of course, is precisely what was happening as quantification conquered the social sciences and, through them, confronted the world of "practical needs." As the economists brought under systematic surveillance the real problems of a modern economy, so the psychologists introduced quantitative rigor into the study of human problems, which had always been considered speculative or ineffable. From animal experiments, psychologists made the great leap to "quantified" propositions about basic human "qualities": intelligence (Binet), memory (Ebbinghaus), conditioning (Pavlov), learning (Thorndike), training (Woodworth), perception (Cannon).[6] Sociologists, starting from the statistical analysis of "social qualities" such as class poverty (Booth) and household budgets (LePlay), soon demonstrated, through aggregative studies of suicide (Durkheim), accidents (Yule), and unhappiness (Jahoda-Zeisl), that the most "qualitative" private decisions could be illuminated by quantifying their public distribution.

These demonstrations by psychologists and sociologists opened the whole universe of private emotion—sexuality and piety, work and wealth, leisure and health—to scientific inquiry through the convergent new discipline of social psychology. With the efflorescence of "attitude research," dealing with opinion formation and attitude change on any matter whatsoever, nothing human was alien to statistical inquiry. The symbolism of quantity now reigned over the full range of human knowledge. Quality was relegated to the defensive ministrations of the humanists-in-retreat.[7]

At the moment of its ascendancy, however, quantity fell victim to doubts and deviations within the scientific community itself. By 1915 Raymond Pearl, a resourceful American biometrician, discussing "the nature of statistical knowledge," was moved to state:

> The writer himself feels in regard to this question [qualification] very far from that serene consciousness of being quite unassailably right which is essential to proper dogmatism. Indeed, it is for the purpose of definitely formulating some doubts, which have grown in the writer's mind during fifteen years in which the greater part of his time and energy have been devoted to the application of statistical methods to biological problems, that this paper is written.[8]

This was written during World War I, a period of great interest for the historic tension between quantity and quality. During just these years, quantification, in the form of applied statistics as proposed by Pearson, was invading social institutions and human relations. Such procedures as the Army Alpha Tests affected the lives of millions of people who were screened, selected, assigned, and promoted according to their numerical results. They certified the new belief that "innate qualities" could be efficiently managed as "social commodities" once their distribution was ascertained by statistical analysis. These very triumphs, however, raised certain questions about quantity that have not yet been fully resolved.

Since these new problems were set by informed scientists, rather than indignant literati, they focused inquiry on searching questions involving the very foundations of mathematical and scientific knowledge. Just as the scientific surge had been built upon confidence in mathematics as the source of valid knowledge, so doubts arose among serious scientists when this confidence was challenged. The propositional content of this intellectual crisis was simple. In a word, it consisted of a new uncertainty whether there was any necessary and direct correspondence between mathematical reality and empirical reality. Mathematical reality, indeed, was leading to conclusions about the nature of our universe which contradicted the evidence of our senses—or, more precisely, that cultural heritage which, from earliest infancy, so tightly shapes our perceptions of the universe that it seems confirmed by our sensuous experience. The findings of physical science, in the past few generations, appeared to set the familiar universe topsy-turvy. It was disquieting to be set in a new world where, as Gilbert and Sullivan put it, "things are seldom what they seem."

The psychocultural problem of adapting oneself to a strange new universe was linked, among scientists, to fundamental questions regarding reality and valid knowledge. A central intellectual issue involved the mathematically related concepts of the continuum and the infinite. The rich literature elaborating these concepts in the past century cannot be adequately summarized in this space, but we may perhaps state the issue concretely enough to clarify the intellectual (and attitudinal) choices it presented to modern thinkers. To do this, we must differentiate the special meanings assigned to quantity and quality in the modern phase of the classic debate.

The key symbols of any debate, long pursued, acquire an array of diverse meanings and a rich cluster of ambiguities. To quantity and quality, in the centuries between the simple preference for quality expressed in *Epistles* and the equally simple but opposite preference for quantity expressed by Jevons, there agglutinated a variety of meanings that are often unrelated and sometimes incompatible. Professor Leontief's paper in this volume refers to "the dialectic juxtaposition" of uniqueness and repetition, abstract theory and concrete description, the singular and the common, the organic and the mechanical, as alternative dichotomies in which the debate has been conducted. So widely has this debate ranged, Leontief warns us, that the original issue of quantity versus quality nowadays "represents only one facet, one stage, of the wider contest between the proponents of concise analytical methods and the defenders of the descriptive individualizing approach."

Professor Thomas S. Kuhn has further specified some historical shifts in the controversy over quantity and quality:

> On some occasions it has meant simply numerical measurement versus the direct apprehension of the senses. On other occasions, under the same rubric, the poverty of scientific abstractions (qualitative or quantitative) is opposed to the sensuous richness of life in the everyday world. At some points the opposition is between the positivist interpretation of

the significance of scientific laws and the "realist" view that such laws give us certain direct information about the "true" structure of the universe. At still other points the opposition is between those who see the universe as an infinite continuum and those who see it as a finite discretum. This last formulation I find particularly puzzling, because in this case I am not even sure which party should be seen as representing quality and which quantity. Though all of these oppositions have been very real and all have had, at one time or another, historical relations to the others, I am at least dubious about the possibility of viewing them all as aspects of some single fundamental historical dichotomy.[9]

This cautionary note is especially compelling in any consideration of the modern debate over quantity and quality. Accordingly, we disregard contemporary variations on old themes—"to count or not to count!"—since these tend to be polemical rather than analytical.[10] We also avoid tracing historical sequences which violate Professor Kuhn's injunction against "some single fundamental historical dichotomy."

Indeed, the distinctively modern perspective tends to ignore the classic dichotomy and to focus, rather, on the *interaction* between qualities and quantities. The concern with interaction is illustrated by the problems of quantifying "discrete," as compared with "continuous," variables. A continuous variable forms an infinitely subdivisible continuum whose defining characteristic (essential properties) is equally present at every point—for example, any amount of water, in any time or place, will manifest the chemical identity H_2O. A discrete variable does not form such a continuum—for example, sweet and sour and saline are "qualitatively" different sensations which exhibit no defining characteristic that remains identical at every point in a continuum of taste.

Such non-continuous (discrete) variables presented difficult empirical and theoretical problems for the mathematics inherited by the nineteenth century. Empirical solutions were found and used—for example, Pearson's determination of "regularities" in the behavior of discrete genes by applied statistics. This process gradually transformed the old dichotomy in such fashion that qualities, now conceived as discrete variables, could more readily be handled as a special case of quantity. Considered as "intensive quantities" which can only be arranged in a serial order, they were easily differentiated empirically from "extensive quantities," which can also be added or combined. Even formal mathematical discrimination was established between "intensive quantities to which numbers can be assigned uniquely up to a monotone transformation, and extensive quantities to which numbers can be assigned uniquely up to a similarity transformation (i.e., multiplication by a positive constant)."[11]

The philosophical transformations that accompanied these alterations of vocabulary and innovations of technique were profound. The modern acceptance of discrete variables and discontinuous continua as amenable to scientific quantification resulted, necessarily, in a reshaping of the traditional conception of nature. Since antiquity, men had conceived the continuum as an essential property of the natural world. The old adage *natura non facit saltus* ("nature does not make jumps") seemed, through the centuries, simply a common-sense expression of a self-evident truth about the real world. This assumption of continuity required the corollary assumption of infinity, or at least the infinitely small. A true natural continuum (air, water, energy) was construed to *mean* infinite *divisibility*. We have seen that in such a continuum any of its parts, however small, would have the essential properties that define the whole. Until the late nineteenth century the findings and methods of science, including its Euclidean mathematics, were compatible with this ancient assumption of continuity-infinity in the universe. In the next half century the scientific view of nature was to be radically reshaped under the impetus, particularly, of modern physics.

With the empirical determination of atomic properties in electricity a half century ago and the subsequent elaboration of nuclear physics, the ancient assumption finally proved incompatible with the intellectual requirements of further scientific inquiry. New conceptions of reality were needed to account for new findings. Macrocosmic phenomena were more readily understandable as statistical aggregates than as natural continua, because they were formed by the highly diversified interactions among microcosmic particles, which were found to behave in apparently erratic and certainly discontinuous ways. Planck, showing that the behavior of energy cannot be accounted for in terms of simple and unlimited divisibility, abandoned the notion of energy continua in favor of energy quanta. Einstein, demonstrating the possibility of a finite world by accounting for all known astronomical results in terms consistent with his hypothesis of an elliptic universe, showed that Euclidean geometry could be superseded by utilizing the *n*-dimensional mathematics of Minkowski and Riemann.

The intellectual impact of abandoning the ancient metaphysics of continuity-infinity was concisely expressed by David Hilbert, who made important contributions to the new mathematics:

> One can indeed regard this emancipation from the infinite as a tendency of modern science. . . . The verdict is that nowhere in reality does there exist a homogeneous continuum in which unlimited divisibility is possible, in which the indefinitely small can be realized. The infinite divisibility of a continuum is an operation which exists in thought only, is just an idea, an idea which is refuted by our observations of nature, as well as by physical and chemical experiments.[12]

But what Hilbert took so easily, others took quite hard. Just as some physicists were greatly disturbed by the loss of classic continua, so some mathematicians were outraged by the loss of familiar infinity. When Georg Cantor replaced infinity by *transfinity,* the conflict erupted:

> And what a struggle! The history of mathematics has not recorded anything equal to it in fury. The stormy beginnings of the theory of aggregates show that even in such an abstract field as mathematics, human emotions cannot be altogether eliminated.[13]

Now that the storm has passed, we can see, with the tranquility of hindsight, that Cantor simply took up and resolved Galileo's paradox. Whereas Galileo ignored the issue he had raised by merely asserting that "the attributes of equal, greater, and less are not applicable to infinite but only to finite quantities," Cantor took this as a point of departure in developing his theory of aggregates. The outcome of Cantor's work, as elaborated by Dedekind, was, expressed summarily, to reduce the ancient metaphysics of finite-infinite series to a single critical difference: In finite aggregates the whole is never equal to a part; in transfinite aggregates a part may be equal to the whole (is not necessarily less).

Cantor's work thus linked the ancient debate over quantity and quality to the other classic problem of parts and wholes. This is another story, with which we shall deal next year in the Hayden Colloquium ("Parts and Wholes" is the general theme for 1959–60). Here we note simply that Cantor, having resolved Galileo's paradox, bequeathed to mathematics a yet more difficult paradox—the paradox that, while we can conceive the aggregate of all aggregates as the last transfinite cardinal, yet there is no operative last transfinite within his system. Around this paradox were ranged two contending schools of mathematical thinkers: the *formalists* (Hilbert, Russell, Zermelo), who sought to restate the theory of aggregates in a purely abstract and internally consistent system without reference to any empirical content; and the *intuitionists* (Kronecker, Brouwer, Weyl), who regarded formalization as an organic disease, antedating Cantorism, by which the whole body mathematical had been affected. Said Weyl: "What is valid seems so insignificant that it may be seriously doubted whether analysis is at all possible."

Between Weyl's hostility and Hilbert's enthusiasm for mathematical formalization, there stretched a gap across which the logical foundations of empirical science teetered uncertainly—not perhaps among scientific practitioners, but certainly among scientific philosophers. If mathematics was only a language for stating formal relations in general terms, without asserting any necessary correspondence between internal "mathematical reality" and the external reality of the natural world, then perhaps the mathematization of empirical science was merely a playful exercise that had led modern knowledge down the garden path. Had not such competent physicists as Eddington and Jeans asserted their belief that the universe was "infinite" and "mysterious," that the capacity of modern mathematics to account for all known data in terms of a finite universe of elliptical orbit merely provided a convenient working hypothesis, not a necessarily true proposition? Did not Heisenberg's principle of indeterminacy—along with relativity, a widely extrapolated and crudely distorted scientific concept—teach us that mathematical rigor could not (any more than experimental rigor) determine the "ultimate truth" about the behavior of the atomic particles of which reality is formed? What bearing, if any, does mathematical reality have upon natural reality? Is mathematics merely a convenient tool for scientists and hence of small interest to the human race, or does it concern all of us because it has some bearing upon truth?[14]

Philosophic Impasse and Scientific Progress

Questions such as these just raised have preoccupied twentieth-century philosophers of science and scientists with philosophical interests. Many solutions have been proposed, some more plausible than others, but none that "solve" these problems with such generality as to win a clear consensus of acceptance among the intellectual community. The philosophic impasse created by scientific progress remains, but scientific progress has continued. The scientific vanguard, after a brief period when some of its members seemed to be detracked, simply shunted the philosophic issues onto a side rail and proceeded empirically along the main roadbed. Contemporary scientists have handled queries derived from the assumption of an "infinite universe" as pseudo-questions by showing that what is known can be efficiently accounted for on the assumption of a finite universe.

The history of science provides other dramatic examples of scientific progress bypassing a philosophic impasse created by itself. The assumption of an inevitable universe (predecessor of the assumption of an infinite universe) persisted for centuries after Pythagoras, who posed the question why the solar orbits *had to be* "just so and only so" as they are. Galileo set this aside as a pseudo-question by showing that these orbits *could have been* otherwise than they are. He was not obliged, however, to abandon the Pythagorean theorem that the square on the longest side of any right-angle triangle is equal to the sum of the squares on the other two sides.

So, while the philosophic impasse created by Galileo's challenge to the idea of an inevitable and finite cosmos persisted, scientific workers made a detour and found a new way. When a new mathematics was needed for the new science—*de reductione scientae ad mathematicam*—Descartes simply ignored the Pythagorean mystique and subsumed its theorem under a larger conception of geometry. Descartes incorporated the visual geometry that had adequately served the Pythagorean concern with length and area into a system which could also deal with distance and space in numerical terms. After Descartes, geometry—and indeed all of mathematics—became known as "the science of space and number."

But in setting aside as "perfectly worthless" the philosophic controversies over infinity and *de compositione continui* which persisted into the seventeenth century, Descartes also pre-empted this strategic terrain for his "intermediate" solution:

> We must never dispute about the infinite, but only hold those things to which we do not find any limit, such as the extension of the world, the divisibility of the parts of matter, the number of stars, etc., to the indefinite. . . . Therefore we shall not bother to answer those who would inquire whether, if there were an infinite line, its half would also be infinite; or whether an infinite number would be even or odd; and such like . . . [in cases where] we are not able to assign any limit, we shall not assert that they are infinite, but we shall consider them as indefinite.[15]

By basing his case on the intermediate concept of indefiniteness, Descartes was able to inter the inevitable finite cosmos, ignore the philosophic impasse around its bier, and develop a system in which "the infinity of the world seems to be established beyond doubt and beyond dispute."

By a similar process the philosophic impasse created by the concept of an infinite universe was in its turn bypassed, yielding solutions for the newer problems preoccupying modern scientists. Riemann abandoned only the Euclidean mystique (which had come to imply an infinite universe) and subsumed its operating concepts under the larger mathematical idea of a "manifold of n-dimensions." He showed that the metaphysical controversy over a finite-infinite universe could safely be ignored for purposes of scientific research by demonstrating that neither assumption was needed to deal efficiently with the scientific problems at hand. He did this by showing that in any set $x_1, x_2, \ldots x_n$, if each term can range over the real number system, a continuous manifold of n dimensions is *generated.* To handle the intermediate case, in which some of the x's vary continuously and the rest discretely, Riemann showed that such a manifold can always be split into a continuous and a discrete manifold. Since there is thus no need to find an independent solution of the intermediate mixed case, Riemann gave contemporary science a fresh example of the old lesson that scientific problems can often be solved by mathematical means even when philosophical analysis leads to an impasse.

H. R. Hertz, who first demonstrated experimentally the existence of wireless waves (a philosophically indeterminate process which had nevertheless been predicted mathematically by Maxwell), expressed this view in naive wonder: "It seems as if the mathematical implements we use are wiser than we, and perform their evolutions independently of our will."[16] Contemporary scientists have become widely aware that the metaphysical dilemmas imposed upon empirical problems tend to become irrelevant once a mathematical (or experimental) solution slips between their horns.

The value of this lesson becomes vivid in the present Colloquium. Riemann's geometry had led mathematics into the study of "manifolds of *n*-dimensions"; empirical problems had led several sciences into the study of multidimensional problems. As often before in intellectual history, science and mathematics converged on problems that baffled men of knowledge in a particular time and place. As often before, philosophic speculation set up an impasse rather than a highway leading toward solutions of these problems. The issue of quantity and quality is no nearer "solution" today than in the day of *Epistles*—if one formulates the issue as is done there. What is philosophically distinctive about contemporary science, however, is its disinterest in dubious dichotomies or disabling dilemmas. When confronted with such classic dichotomies as quantity versus quality, scientists nowadays shrug their shoulders and proceed to investigate mathematically or empirically the intermediate, mixed, deviant—in short, the limiting—cases. They work with latent or explicit trichotomies, which demonstrate, at the very least, that dichotomous formulations rarely help and often hinder the quest for knowledge.

Riemann's idea of a "manifold of *n*-dimensions"—and his demonstration that the mixed case (combining both discrete and continuous variables) could be solved mathematically if not philosophically—is a nice example of this process. For the current convergence of mathematics and science on multidimensional problems could occur only on the heels of such a break-through. What followed was the development of protomathematical matrices. These matrices involve the formal arrangement of qualitative variates ("qualities" lacking empirical "quantities") in such manner as to generate significant numerical values which permit ranking and scaling of the variates. In this way—by mathematical techniques which predict the *limits within which* any empirically determined magnitudes would have to lie—science has bypassed the philosophic impasse. It handles multidimensional "qualitative" relationships by adapting the powerful methods of "quantitative" research through the ingenuity of formal mathematics. Under the title of "models"—matrices in search of magnitudes—leading thinkers in every discipline have been at work developing these techniques during recent years. The outcome of their work is presented in the papers that compose this volume.

The Matter in Hand

Appropriately enough, Professor John G. Kemeny opens the Colloquium with a paper on "Mathematics without Numbers." This is a very new note indeed, for it invites our attention to the feasibility of mathematizing qualities without first quantifying them. Concerned with utilizing mathematical analysis for the solution of realistic multidimensional problems, Kemeny ignores dead-end philosophic issues and presents four specific models applicable to current issues in the social sciences. The first is relevant to the general problem of "structural balance" in a social group. Accepting the empirical definition that groups are effectively in balance when the like-dislike relationships between pairs of members are reciprocal, Kemeny shows how the empirical results may be formalized and generalized by application of the structure theorem for signed graphs. This procedure yields a simple model drawn from graph theory, a branch of modern geometry which can handle "qualitative relations" of the like-dislike type without resort to number and space concepts. Generalizing from the model to political behavior, Kemeny suggests the interesting inference that "a political body is balanced if, and only if, it is possible to impose a two-party structure on it."

For his second problem, involving the codification of marriage rules in primitive societies, Kemeny adapts the concept of a "group of transformations" from group theory, a branch of modern algebra which requires no numbers at all. Again, by putting the empirical definition of marriage types and rules of intermarriage into mathematical form, Kemeny is able to apply an established theorem for regular permutation groups and thus "to find easily all possible marriage rules for a given number of marriage types. For example, it is shown that there are but six possible sets of rules for a society having four marriage types. It is then interesting to note that two of these are actually in use in the Tarau and the Kariera societies respectively." Because the algebra of transformation groups produces a comprehensive array of all possible combinations and permutations under any given set of conditions, Kemeny can even suggest available alternatives to improve the efficacy of the rules actually governing Tarau and Kariera marriages. He thus provides an interesting example of mathematical contribution to the "policy sciences"—the quest, through scientific inquiry, for useful alternative solutions to social problems that are not found through unaided experience and common sense.

The third example introduces a matrix to formalize the ranking of transmission-reception positions in a communication network. Although the matrix is merely a square array of numbers, with as many rows and columns as there are persons in the network, its introduction of "contrived" numbers permits those simple arithmetical operations whereby Kemeny can formulate a rule for ranking as many as one hundred communications in a network—an impossible task for "qualitative" methods unaided by "quantitative" techniques.

The final example shows how geometrical tools help to solve a classic quantitative problem which was not previously considered geometrical in character. This is the recurrent "panel problem" of determining a consensus-ranking from diverse judgments on a multidimensional array of items. Kemeny handles the concrete example by formalizing the conditions governing the judgments expressed by ten judges who independently ranked a set of fifty objects in order of preference. Using two alternate procedures—minimizing the sums of the distances between individual rankings or the sums of the squares of these distances—Kemeny presents an ingenious way out of the logico-mathematical difficulty defined by K. J. Arrow's General Possibility Theorem. Arrow showed that any reasonable method of consensus-ranking must occasionally give multiple answers—that is, an *indeterminate* consensus-ranking. Kemeny's methods, while satisfying Arrow's conditions of reasonableness and granting the occasional indeterminacy they impose, yet appear to give unique answers for some types of consensus-ranking problems. Because this is a central methodological concern in handling multidimensional problems of the social sciences, Kemeny's fourth model will be extremely helpful to those engaged in empirical social research. Although an elegant general solution of the Arrow problem is yet to be found, Kemeny's work enables researchers to get on with their work instead of marking time until such a general solution is discovered.

Professor Victor F. Weisskopf, in discussing philosophical problems that concern quantum physics, indicates that the classic dichotomy of quality versus quantity was formulated in terms that are now largely irrelevant. The contemporary physicist finds little utility in the traditional antinomies which presented sort versus size, mode versus measure, as mutually exclusive categories of analysis. Such categories become meaningless when the quality under discussion is a "quantum state," whose mode is defined by its measure, whose sort is a function of its size, and whose quality, in short, *is* its quantity. The important task is rather to develop analytic categories which take account of the interaction between quantity and quality. For this purpose, the significant variable to be differentiated is discreteness and continuity. Professor Weisskopf proposes the vivid image of a "quantum ladder," which enables him to locate discrete items within continuous manifolds. A rung without a ladder loses its specific function; a ladder missing a rung can tumble the person who climbs it. In an interesting passage, he indicates a linkage between modern physical theory and the Pythagorean "pre-established harmony." He then concisely epitomizes the distinctive environment of modern physical science: "But this time [the 'harmony' is] clearly understood as a vibration phenomenon of confined electron waves."

The absorbing account of the "quantification of sensation," by Professor S. S. Stevens, while linked at points with Weisskopf's philosophic position, exhibits the general problem of quantity and quality in a form and at a level appropriate to our state of knowledge about the problems domesticated in experimental psychology. What could be more "qualitative"—in the sense of unique—than the sensory experience of a single ear or eye? Yet, when individuals in a sample compare their unique eye-and-ear sensations under experimental control, there emerge certain quantitative "regularities" that enable Stevens to reach for formal generalizations. He speaks of "some beautifully simple laws of sensory action," these being "quantitative laws" made possible by "the orderly manner in which observers have performed the task of cross-modality matching."

A striking aspect of Stevens' presentation is the systematic effort to match empirical operations with mathematical relationships. Using only mathematical group theory, Stevens identifies four kinds of scales with four types of "mathematical group-structure": permutation, isotonic, linear, and similarity. The nature of these four scales of measurement determines the "permissible statistics" that can be used in empirical studies on the psychology of sensation (see his Table 1). That psychologists today have successfully defied the dictum of their eminent predecessors, who said that sensations could not be measured, Stevens attributes to the current recognition that "measurement is not limited to counting." The new conception of quantification derives, in turn, from "the formal emancipation of mathematics, its complete decoupling from matters of empirical, earthy fact."

Once equipped with appropriate new concepts and techniques of measurement, psychologists proceeded to measure sensations despite the "troop of old ghosts" clustered defensively "around the issue of privacy." Dealing with sensation as an object of public scrutiny and mensuration required some new definitions of old concepts. Says Stevens: "Perhaps the chief of these distinctions is that between quantity and quality. . . . what it means concretely is that sweet is different from sour, although both may vary from strong to weak." Psychophysics soon found that it could say little about qualitative variations among sensations, which appear to occur in a "succession of baffling and discontinuous leaps." There is a poignant recognition of quality's challenge to quantification, akin to Weisskopf's presentation of the quantum states, in Stevens' succinct declaration: "Sometimes a crude ordering seems possible, but for the most part the qualities are just what they are, and the best we can do is to name them."

With those aspects of sensation that can be arranged on a continuum of some sort, where the metrical tools of mathematics can be applied, psychophysics has made long strides. Stevens reports that the results obtained by experiments on some two dozen sensory continua regularly behave according to the "power law": the sensation magnitude grows as a power function of the stimulus magnitude. One may reserve judgment on the generality of this law or on the importance of the results that illustrate it. But when, in previously unquantified relationships, variation can be associated with an exponent *n*, in an equation where the constant *k* depends only on the units of measurement, then noteworthy metrical work is in progress.

Professor Walter A. Rosenblith faces squarely the philosophic issues we have outlined in his analytic review of current research on neuroelectric behavior in organisms. That research progress has been made, without involvement in the philosophic impasse, is indicated by his lively discussion of "the data-rich and theory-poor" state of this field. Rosenblith makes quite clear the irrelevance of the classic dichotomies for scientists who seek "measurements reflecting the behavior of complex systems." He acknowledges the "preference for packaging our results in a form that is reasonably quantitative." But he cautions against a preference turned "prejudice" that would render the neurophysicist so "narrow-minded as to ignore the usefulness and even the beauty of a good classification scheme."

Qualitative operations of identification, classification, and comparison are all needed to deal, for example, with the "complex system" of a vowel sound. Despite the different spectral components of an "*ah*" when pronounced by men, women, children, or even when repeated by the same person, "something invariant" identifies it as an "ah." How is one to define this quality? Says Rosenblith: "This 'ah'-ness is not anything that is really characterizable by absolute numbers, but rather by distinctive features or parametrically defined patterns, by certain relations among the components of a sound, especially in relation to other sounds that might have been emitted."

Although mathematics alone yields "parametrically defined patterns," it is a mathematics adapted to qualitative variables that Rosenblith has in mind. The reader, fresh from Kemeny's paper on "mathematics without numbers," will be alert to the reminder of Gödel's dictum that "it is purely an historical accident that mathematics developed along quantitative lines." However this may be, we comprehend why Rosenblith stresses the qualitative in the present state of neurophysiology: "We are aiming to discover the relevant units of analysis, those distinctive features of neural signals that will help us to put order into the innumerable data that we can record from the nervous system." This requires the full range of mathematical analysis, from classification through rank-ordering to metrical techniques. Rosenblith shares the distinctively modern concern with mathematization of qualities that is expressed by Kemeny, Weisskopf, and Stevens.

Such a concern, we have seen, bypasses the traditional dichotomies underlying the philosophic impasse. Rosenblith has little interest in considering continuous versus discrete variables as mutually exclusive, for "every reductionist scheme runs sooner or later into the perplexing problem of recoding continuity into discreteness and discreteness into continuity." Nor is the idea of "an infinitely divisible continuum" an indispensable initial condition for empirical research. Indeed, the basic dichotomy of quantity versus quality becomes irrelevant when confronted by the neuro-electrical performance of "man and his closest relatives in the animal kingdom," since their transition from categorical to *vernier* modes, from multivariate qualitative to more quantitative judgments, is apparently quite smooth. "It thus becomes both idle and artificial to cut this continuum of performance in the informational domain by telling us that now man quantifies, and now he only categorizes [qualifies]." Not philosophical dichotomies but "pluralist" research strategies, Rosenblith counsels us, will advance our knowledge of the "complex systems."

Professors Leontief and Lasswell, who confront the problem of quantity and quality on a level more complex than individual reactions to discrete stimuli experimentally controlled, deal with key systems of social life: the economic system of distributing wealth, and the political system of distributing power. Their common concern with quantification derives from their shared interest in "aggregates" formed by specified individuals behaving in specified ways in specified situations. There is, however, a significant difference in the level of quantification achieved by the sciences of which they speak.

Professor Wassily Leontief deals with economics, long recognized among the social sciences as the "quantitative science *par excellence.*" Quantification in economics "is more than a methodological device, it is also an object of the inquiry itself." Quantitative analysis is not restricted to "those aspects of the economic process which involve directly observed, consciously . . . quantifying attitudes." According to Leontief:

> Some of the most advanced applications of mathematical methods in economics are found in the fields of general equilibrium analysis and business-cycle theory—both recognized as quasi-mechanical, automatic phenomena formed and operating to a large extent beyond the calculations, outside the control of, and mostly against the wills of the millions of individuals whom they affect.

Economists have achieved this capacity to deal with aggregates of human behavior, independent of particular individuals in the aggregate, by defining two conditions by which the effective behavior of *all* individuals must be limited: the production function and the consumption function. In this way the economist "reduces the qualitative complexity (the dimensionality) of the material with which he will have to deal from then on. He retains only those variables the magnitudes of which affect *directly* either the costs incurred in, or the revenue received from, the operation of the production process he describes."

The method works in all cases where its assumption, that rationality in the economic system acts as a limit upon variations of individual behavior, is self-confirming. As Leontief puts it: "The profit-maximizing producer can be expected to adjust the magnitudes of all the 'nonpriced' variables in such a way as to attain an efficient relationship between the quantities of the priced variables." The producer who does not behave according to this expectation is usually ejected from the economic system and re-enters it, if at all, in a different role. "Special cases" where political purpose takes priority over economic rationality—as in some totalitarian and underdeveloped countries—operate by a different mechanism and must be considered separately.

Once the underlying mechanism is operative, with all the possibilities it opens for algebraic substitutions and other mathematical manipulations, the economist turns to the consumption (or utility) function. This he sees, according to Leontief, as "essentially a question of introduction or omission of an auxiliary variable and of a corresponding reformulation of a given system of theoretical relationships." To deal with the majestic philosophic question of "utility," then, the economist can rely only on his workaday, empirically derived index numbers of consumption. At this point, however, the economist has refined his techniques enough to land himself in a predicament akin to that which the Boltzmann paradox and Heisenberg principle impose upon the physicist concerned with quantum states. Leontief writes:

> The reduction in qualitative variety is attained at the cost of ever increasing quantitative indeterminacy; as we have seen, the more general the contents of an index number, the more vague and arbitrary will its measure be. . . . When one speaks in general of "appliances" instead of "consumers' durables," one excludes automobiles but leaves unspecified whether one has in mind refrigerators, washing machines, or TV sets; and when one speaks of refrigerators, one still omits the distinction between those run by electricity and those operated by gas.

In formulating so sharply "the highly speculative and—what is worse—essentially unsolvable problems of so-called index-number theory," Leontief shows us how far, in fact, economic science has come. It continues to make research progress despite its arrival at the modern philosophic impasse.

Professor Harold D. Lasswell takes up the problems of index formation in the less highly developed field of political inquiry. The science of power has not yet attained the level of methodological sophistication which is operative in the science of wealth. Hence, whereas Leontief speaks of the insoluble theoretical problems of index numbers, in terms reminiscent of Kemeny's indeterminate "consensus-rankings," Weisskopf's inviolate "quantum states," and Stevens' insoluble "qualitative variations," Lasswell enjoins a science still largely innocent of mathematical analysis to learn how index formation may advance studies of power. As an astute observer of scientific history, Lasswell is aware that formalization will eventually land political science in methodological predicaments similar to those current in the more advanced sciences: "The challenge to translate general conceptions into operational indexes . . . typically brings into focus the usefulness of introducing a series of intermediate categories of diminishing generality."

This is the counsel of systematic multidimensionality, which alerts political scientists to seek ways of avoiding (or postponing) the philosophic impasse soon reached in every science that formalizes its empirical substance exclusively through dichotomous concepts. Lasswell's advocacy of a "configurative method" is a direct challenge to the view that political behavior (simply because it is a form of human behavior) is not amenable to scientific scrutiny which is both realistic and systematic. Lasswell proposes to bypass this philosophic impasse based on the putative "nature" of human behavior—which is merely an untested assertion long taken for granted—in much the same manner that Riemann bypassed the assumption of infinite space built into geometry by Euclid. Just as Riemann broke through with the idea of an "*n*-dimensional manifold," so Lasswell proposes a multidimensional "event-manifold." As Riemann showed that the ancient dilemma of discrete and continuous manifolds could be solved (or at least escaped) by handling the variables independently, so Lasswell proposes that *both* uniqueness and regularity in human behavior be conceived as "real" and compatible, even though our methodological limitations now oblige us to study them separately and by different procedures.

Clinical study of the *unique* "manifold of events" constituted by a single case does not require, in any known logic, that we reject the reality or utility of studying the *recurrent* "manifolds" presented by a set of cases. Nor does the statistical analysis of regularity in human behavior cause, outside the polemics of embattled humanists out to "save" human uniqueness, the "individual experience to wither away in the whir of IBM machines." The whir of IBM machines does nothing whatsoever to any individual experience, except to enable observers to collate and compare it with other individual experiences. Stevens' studies of regularity in sensation do not change any individual's experience by an iota; they only increase the psychophysicist's capacity to understand what is common and variant (regular and unique) in the human experience of sensation. Nor do Erikson's rich studies of pathology in individual cases, discussed in last year's Hayden Colloquium on "Evidence and Inference," exclude the knowledge gained by studying regularities. The lesson, as Paul E. Meehl concludes from a careful analysis of "clinical vs. statistical prediction" in psychology, is this: "There is no convincing reason to assume that explicitly formalized mathematical rules and the clinician's creativity are equally suited for any given kind of task, or that their comparative effectiveness is the same for different tasks."[18]

At a minimum, the clinician's "insight" can be validated only by the statistician's "tests." In this sense, Meehl warns the clinician, "*always* the actuary will have the final word" with respect to validation. On a higher level, the quantitative "regularity" can help to determine the "unique" quality by which its own recurrence is governed. The situation calls, in Rosenblith's phrase, for "pluralistic research strategies."

The essential point, for Professor Lasswell, is to recognize "the indispensable role performed by the qualitative as well as the quantitative in the tasks of inquiry." Students of political behavior, using the best tools available for the problem at hand, must define each problem within an adequate multidimensional context. This is the meaning of his call for "systematic multivalued models of the social process." The political scientist who practices "systematic functionalism" will find his choice of research methods, including mathematical tools now not widely used, governed by the requirements of his more rigorously defined and amply formalized problems. Lasswell concludes:

> Creative tension between the qualitative and the quantitative becomes of increasing rather than diminishing importance as we perfect comprehensive and continuing intelligence surveys of world social progress, and use more "intensive" tools to disclose the structure of predisposition in every principal context.

That the ancient dichotomy between mutually exclusive quantity and quality is now conceived as a "creative tension" between reciprocal ways of knowing bespeaks a deep transformation in the structure of modern thought. If the mechanistic and quantitative universe of nineteenth-century science has vanished, as is often alleged, it has left profound traces in contemporary thinking. The concern with quality among scientists today does not simply reinstate the prescientific epistemology of some earlier era. The modern synthesis seeks rather to reshape, for more productive use, two components of knowledge which can no longer be efficiently maintained in dialectical opposition.

The philosophic perspective of the past century assumed causality, inferred that the whole is the sum of its parts, and concluded that valid knowledge is quantitative. Contemporary scientists tend to be less concerned with causes than with consequences, investigate wholes which are "more than" (cannot be expressed adequately as) the sum of their parts, and accord equal status, as valid knowledge, to qualitative classifications (which may be classes of numbers, as in Weisskopf's quantum states) and to quantitative measurements.

The central tendency of current scientific thinking may be leading, as Peter F. Drucker supposes, to "a discipline that explains events and phenomena in terms of their direction and future state rather than in terms of cause—a calculus of potential, you might say, rather than one of probability."[19] Many streams, rising from independent sources but flowing in a common direction, contribute to such an intellectual confluence. New ideas that rethink the ancient dichotomies of quantity and quality, parts and wholes, cause and effect—these are major tributaries in reshaping the stream of contemporary thought. The present volume continues the discussion initiated last year in *Evidence and Inference.* In our consideration of "parts and wholes" next year, we shall extend this rethinking of traditional concepts and methods which is the aim of the Hayden Colloquium.

NOTES

1. Quoted in Morris Kline, *Mathematics in Western Culture,* New York: Oxford, 1953, p. 3.
2. Quoted by Daniel Lerner, in R. K. Merton and P. F. Lazarsfeld (eds.), *Continuities in Social Research,* Glencoe: The Free Press, 1951, p. 249.
3. W. S. Jevons, *The Theory of Political Economy,* London, 1888, p. xx.
4. Tobias Dantzig, *Number: The Language of Science,* New York: Macmillan, 1949, p. 232.
5. Karl Pearson, *The Grammar of Science,* London: Dent, 1937, p. xii.
6. See H. E. Garrett, *Great Experiments in Psychology,* New York: Century, 1930.
7. See Daniel Lerner, "Social Science: Whence and Whither?" *The Human Meaning of the Social Sciences,* New York: Meridian, 1959.
8. Raymond Pearl, *Modes of Research in Genetics,* New York: Macmillan, 1915, p. 75.
9. Personal communication. I am indebted to Professor Kuhn for valuable criticism of the historical sections of this paper.

10. A detailed case study of "scientific polemics" on this theme is reported in my chapter in Merton and Lazarsfeld, *op. cit.*

11. Patrick Suppes, "A Set of Independent Axioms for Extensive Quantities," *Portugaliae Mathematica*, 1951, *10.*

12. Quoted in Dantzig, *op. cit.*, p. 238. Chapter 12 gives a clear statement of the debate over mathematical "infinity" as set forth in Hilbert's "Ueber das Unendliche," in *Grundlagen der Geometry* (Leipzig, 1930), and in Couturat's *De l'infini mathematique* (Paris, 1896).

13. Dantzig, *op. cit.*, p. 212. See also Cantor's *Contributions to the Founding of Transfinite Numbers,* Chicago: Open Court, 1915.

14. See H. T. Davis, "A Survey of the Problem of Mathematical Truth," Introduction to Helmholz's *Counting and Measuring,* Princeton: Van Nostrand, 1930.

15. Alexander Koyré, *From the Closed World to the Infinite Universe,* Baltimore: Johns Hopkins, 1957, pp. 106–107.

16. E. T. Bell, *Mathematics: Queen and Servant of Science,* New York: McGraw-Hill, 1951, p. xv.

17. K. J. Arrow, *Social Choice and Individual Values,* New York: Wiley, 1951, ch. 5.

18. P. A. Meehl, *Clinical versus Statistical Prediction,* Minneapolis: University of Minnesota, 1954, pp. vi, 138.

19. P. F. Drucker, *Landmarks of Tomorrow,* New York: Harper, 1959, p. 15.

Mathematics without Numbers

JOHN G. KEMENY

A HUNDRED years ago a mathematician would have defined mathematics as "the study of number and space." Indeed, the Thorndike-Barnhart *Dictionary* published in 1956 still defines mathematics as the "science dealing with numbers and the measurement, properties, and relationships of quantities." The study of numbers led to the development of algebra, and the study of space to geometry. These two disciplines merged in the calculus, the crowning glory of classical mathematics. A significant feature of modern mathematics is that such a definition is much too narrow to include its newer branches.

Classical mathematics was ideally suited for the development of physics. Indeed, it arose from physics in many cases. For innumerable problems in physics on which measurements are readily available, the physicist may use a numerical model. On other problems the physicist is concerned with the nature of physical space, and thus classical geometry is suitable as a model. Even when Euclidean geometry proved to be no longer adequate for the needs of modern physics, Einstein was able to use a mathematical model which combined a non-Euclidean geometry with methods of the calculus. This type of model still fits the description of mathematics as the study of number and space.

The social sciences may be characterized by the fact that in most of their problems numerical measurements seem to be absent and considerations of space are irrelevant. I would like to consider in this paper ways in which mathematical models may be used in connection with typical problems in the social sciences.

Let us consider why a scientist employs mathematical form in which to formulate scientific theories. It forces the theoretician in various sciences to formulate his hypotheses in a precise and unambiguous form. It also forces him to strip the scientific problem of all accidental details. Once the model is formulated in its abstract form, it becomes a branch of mathematics. If the scientist is fortunate, this branch of mathematics will have been studied by mathematicians previously, and then theorems proven in this field become available as predictions for the scientist. For the axioms of the mathematical system, when interpreted, represent scientific theories, and hence the theorems, when interpreted in the same way, are logical consequences of the scientist's theories. In this way the mathematician will have accomplished the logical analysis of scientific theories for the scientist.

It has often been pointed out that the mathematical theorem adds nothing to the hypotheses from which it is deduced. Indeed, if a theorem added to the content of the hypotheses, it would not follow logically from them, and hence it would not be a theorem of the branch of mathematics. However, theorems, though not new in content, may be psychologically new to the scientist, and very often are. In effect, the mathematician says to the scientist, "Did you know that your assumptions imply such and such?" And very often this will come as a pleasant (or unpleasant) surprise to the scientist. The mathematician has bridged the gap between original assumptions and verifiable predictions. He has enabled the scientist to test his hypotheses, and often enables him to make pragmatically significant predictions about the future.

But it sometimes happens that the mathematical model formulated by the scientist does not correspond to any known branch of mathematics. In this case the scientist either must create a new branch of mathematics or must appeal to the mathematician to undertake this task for him. For example, when Newton formulated his Laws of Motion, he found that there was no branch of mathematics suitable for the treatment of his new model. He had to turn to the method of the calculus that he invented. The social scientist today often finds the mathematician unable to enlighten him on the particular model of interest to him. Many mathematicians have the impression that mathematical problems in the social sciences are entirely trivial. On the contrary, most problems in the social sciences are too difficult for present-day mathematics. It is because the problems arising in the social sciences rapidly become difficult that only some of the very simplest mathematical problems have been solved so far.

There is every reason to expect that the various social sciences will serve as incentives for the development of great new branches of mathematics and that some day the theoretical social scientist will have to know more mathematics than the physicist needs to know today.

There are essentially two different ways in which a mathematical model may be formed for a problem that does not involve numbers or space. The first method is to use a branch of mathematics which itself does not employ numbers and does not deal with space. The second method is to introduce numbers by a more or less arbitrary method, where no numbers were at first apparent. Then it may be possible to form a significant numerical model of a nonnumerical problem. Two examples of each of these approaches will be discussed in detail below.

The examples to be discussed will employ methods either from modern algebra or from modern geometry. To give a maximum variety to these examples, one algebraic and one geometric model will be discussed for each of the two possible approaches to nonnumerical problems.

Model No. 1

Our first model will employ graph theory, which is a branch of modern geometry, but it may be said to be in no way relevant to the study of space. Thus we will discuss a geometric example of a model in which the problem, to start with, is nonnumerical and nonspatial, and the model formed remains so. The problem to be considered is that of structural balance in a social group.[1]

We consider a social group with certain information concerning likes and dislikes between pairs of individuals. A graph is a convenient mathematical language in which to represent such a structure.

A *graph* is defined as a set of points with lines connecting some, though not necessarily all, pairs of points. We may allow some of these lines to have arrows on them indicating directions, in which case we speak of a *directed graph.* We may also allow plus and minus signs on some of these lines, in which case we speak of a *signed graph.* If persons A and B are represented by two points, then an arrow from A to B with a plus sign might indicate that A likes B, and one with a minus sign might indicate that A dislikes B. If there is no arrow from A to B, then A is indifferent to B (see Figure 1).

A + B   A B   A — B

Figure 1

In the problem to be considered we will be interested in conditions under which a social group is in "balance." If A likes B but B does not like A, then there is a lack of balance. The first necessary condition for balance will be that B should always hold the same relation to A that A holds to B. Therefore we need not employ directed graphs; ordinary signed graphs will serve our purpose. These graphs, which have no arrow on the line segments, are suitable for symmetric relations.

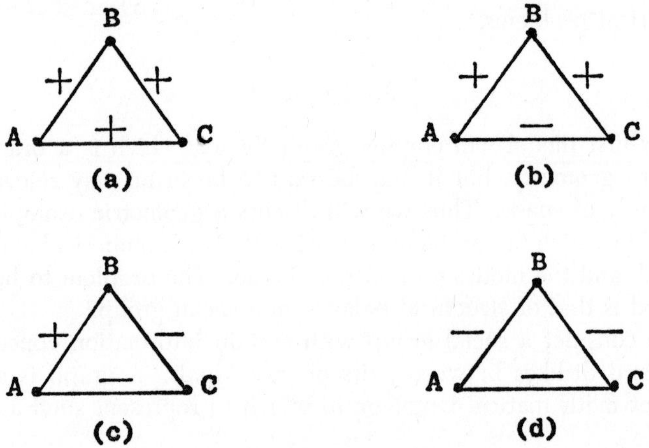

Figure 2

Figure 2 represents the possible signed graphs for three people if no person is indifferent to any other person. In (a), where everyone likes everyone else, the social group is balanced. In (b), where person B likes both the others, but these two dislike each other, there is an unbalanced situation. In (c), A and B like each other and each of them dislikes the third person. This is again a balanced situation. Graph (d) represents a situation in which everyone dislikes everyone else. This may be considered to be unbalanced, as there will be strong forces for pairs of individuals to form a coalition against the third one. It may be observed that the graphs with an even number of minus signs are balanced and the graphs with an odd number of minus signs are unbalanced.

Cartwright and Harary searched the literature for examples in which social scientists had labeled social groups "balanced" or "unbalanced." They noted that all these situations satisfied the following definition: If we take a *cycle* within a graph to be a path starting at A and ending at A, we then define a signed graph to be *balanced* if every cycle in it has an even number of minus signs.

Since this definition subsumed every example they found in the literature, and since it provided a complete definition of balanced social structures, they proposed it as a general definition of structural balance in a social group. Of course it remains for the social scientists to decide whether this is a satisfactory general definition. Let us assume for the moment that it is.

We now have a mathematical model for structural balance in a social group. Since we have the tools of graph theory available to us, let us search for a theorem of graph theory that would lead to an interesting conclusion concerning social groups. Such an example is the *structure theorem* for signed graphs. This theorem may be stated as follows: A signed graph is balanced if, and only if, it is possible to subdivide the points into two sets, such that all positive connections occur between points in the same set and all negative connections occur between points in different sets.

This theorem has a most interesting interpretation in terms of political science. Let us suppose that we have a political body with likes, dislikes, and indifferences between pairs of members. Or, if we prefer, we may replace likes by "ability to get along politically." Let us say that "it is possible to impose a two-party structure" on the political body if there is a method of dividing the members of the political body into two parties, so that any one member likes members only of his own party and dislikes members only of the other party. This holds under the alternate interpretation if any one member can get along only with members of his own party and fails to get along politically only with members of the opposing party. Then the structure theorem says simply that a political body is balanced if, and only if, it is possible to impose a two-party structure on it.

This result, which may be surprising to the social scientist, is a good example of the pure mathematician contributing a useful theorem.

Model No. 2

The second model employs group theory, a branch of modern algebra in which numbers need play no role at all. Specifically, we will be concerned with a group of transformations.

A *group of transformations* may be characterized as follows: We are given a set of objects S and a certain collection G of "changes" on S. That is, each element of G may be used to change an object of S into some other (or possibly the same) object of S. For these transformations G to form a *group*, two conditions must be satisfied. First, the changes must come in pairs: for every transformation g_1 there must be a transformation g_2, so that g_2 always undoes what g_1 did, and vice versa. That is, if g_1 changes an object s into an object t, then g_2 must change the object t into the object s. The second condition is that the result of performing two transformations, one after the other, should again be a transformation within G. Thus if g_1 takes s into t, and g_2 takes t into u, then g_3 will change s directly into u. This may be thought of simply as a mental attitude on our part, in that we always decide to include the "combined transformation" g_3 in our collection G.

The reader will note the extremely general nature of the concept of a group of transformations. Yet there is a vast literature on groups of transformations, and hence a tremendous number of theorems that may be employed any time such a group is available to us.

Marriage rules in primitive societies have been studied from a mathematical point of view by André Weil and Robert R. Bush.[2] The marriage rules in certain primitive societies are designed to prevent marriage between close relatives, even when these relatives are not aware of the fact that they are related. This is desirable in a society where no exact records are kept and where family ties may soon be forgotten. The basic rule is that each person in the society is assigned a certain "marriage type" and that a man may marry a woman only if she is of his own type. Given the type of the parents, each son is assigned one definite type and each daughter is assigned another definite type.

We immediately see that brother-sister marriages are automatically forbidden in this society, since a son from a given marriage is always assigned a different type from that of a daughter.

Our basic set of objects is the set of marriage types. Our transformations will be rules according to which we find the type of a relative of a person, knowing the type of the person. Since a relative of a relative is again a relative, the result of applying two transformations will again be a transformation. Furthermore, if there is a transformation changing the type of an uncle to that of a nephew, there should also be a transformation that changes the type of a nephew to that of an uncle, and hence both conditions are satisfied for having a group of transformations.

Among the conditions of reasonableness for marriage types, the two most important conditions not yet mentioned are: "For any two individuals it is permissible for some of their descendants to intermarry"; and "The rule as to whether a man is allowed to marry a female relative of a given kind depends only on the kind of relationship." The former assures that the society does not split into castes, and the latter assures that there is no discrimination against a given marriage type.

We now have a mathematical model for marriage rules in primitive societies, and we may search the mathematical literature for appropriate theorems applicable to this problem. The basic result is that the marriage group must be a regular permutation group which is generated by the parent-to-son transformation and by the parent-to-daughter transformation. Since regular permutation groups are relatively rare, this theorem enables one to find easily all possible marriage rules for a given number of marriage types. For example, it is shown that there are but six possible sets of rules for a society having four marriage types. It is then interesting to note that two of these are actually in use in the Tarau and the Kariera societies respectively.

For example, in the Kariera society, the parent-to-son transformation interchanges types, 1, 2, and 3, 4, while the parent-to-daughter transformation reverses the order of the types (see Table 1). If we have parents of type 2, a son will have type 4, and his daughters will have type 1. A daughter of the original parents will have type 3, and her sons will also have type 1. Hence a son of the daughter of given parents will be allowed to marry the daughter of a son. The same is true no matter what type the grandparents are.

TABLE 1

Type Numbers in Kariera Society

Parents	*Son*	*Daughter*
1	3	4
2	4	3
3	1	2
4	2	1

The model also suggests certain additional questions one may not have thought of in an informal formulation of the problem. For example, both the above-mentioned societies allow certain first-cousin marriages, though other first-cousin marriages are forbidden. It would be reasonable to impose an additional restriction that first-cousin marriages should always be forbidden. In this case one can prove that the necessary and sufficient condition for this is that parent-to-son and parent-to-daughter transformations should not commute and that their squares should not be equal. These additional conditions eliminate all regular groups with less than six types. Therefore we find that the Kariera and Tarau societies could not possibly have eliminated all first-cousin marriages if they wanted to use only four types.

This example is historically very interesting and illuminating. It is most impressive that a society that is unable to keep precise records should have been able to solve, through trial and error, a problem that requires fairly intricate mathematical operations for formal analysis. It also shows, however, that their procedures could have been considerably improved if they had been in a position to use modern algebra to design the rules. For example, they could have eliminated all first-cousin marriages.

We have just considered models in which numbers are not used and in which no geometry occurs. Now we shall consider others in which numbers or geometric concepts are artificially introduced: Model No. 3 will be numerical and Model No. 4 geometrical.

Model No. 3

Let us consider a communication network. By this we mean a set of people with certain means of sending messages from one to the other. For each pair of people i and j it may be possible to send a message from i to j, from j to i, in both directions, or in neither direction. It would at first appear that this is a situation in which no numbers could ever be usefully introduced. However, a simple numerical model for communication networks has proved fruitful.

We introduce a square array of numbers, known as a matrix, which has as many rows and columns as there are people in our network. Let us call this matrix C and let us call the entry in the ith row and the jth columns $c_{i,j}$; $c_{i,j}$ will be chosen to be 1 if it is possible to send a message directly from i to j; otherwise $c_{i,j}=0$. In particular, we will always choose $c_{i,i}=0$, which is merely a convention. (That is, by definition, a person cannot send himself a message.)

It is immediately clear that all the information available to us about the communication network is furnished by the matrix. However, any number of other methods could be thought of that would represent this information just as well. Has anything been gained by introducing numbers? Numbers are truly useful only if arithmetical operations are introduced. For example, matrices can be multiplied; in particular, we can multiply the matrix C by itself. According to the customary rules of matrix multiplication, we will then find that the entry in the ith row in the jth column of the new matrix will give us the number of different ways in which i can send a message to j in two steps.

In Figure 3 we show communication matrix C for a network of four people in which 1 can communicate directly with 2, 2 can communicate directly with all three of the others, 3 can communicate directly with 4, and 4 can communicate directly with 1 and 3. We also show in the same figure C^2, which indicates the number of ways a given man can communicate with other men in two steps. For example, 2 can communicate with each man in two steps in just one way.

$$C = \begin{Bmatrix} 0 & 1 & 0 & 0 \\ 1 & 0 & 1 & 1 \\ 0 & 0 & 0 & 1 \\ 1 & 0 & 1 & 0 \end{Bmatrix} \qquad C^2 = \begin{Bmatrix} 1 & 0 & 1 & 1 \\ 1 & 1 & 1 & 1 \\ 1 & 0 & 1 & 0 \\ 0 & 1 & 0 & 1 \end{Bmatrix}$$

Figure 3

The fruitfulness of such a model might of course be judged in terms of theorems that can be proved about it. An interesting theorem[3] concerns a complete communication network. By this we mean that, for each pair of people i and j, it is possible to send a message either from i to j, or from j to i, or in both directions. For such a complete communication network there is a simple interpretation for having the largest number of ones in a given row. For example, in Figure 3 (which shows a complete network) man 2 has the largest row sum, namely 3. The proof shows that the person whose row in the matrix has the largest row sum can communicate with everyone in the network in one or two steps. Of course, in Figure 3 man 2 can actually do this in a single step.

This system has an interesting mathematical feature known as duality—namely, by interchanging rows and columns it is possible to change a matrix of "can send a message to" to a matrix of "can receive a message from." The above-quoted theorem is still applicable to the dual matrix, and hence we know that if a given person's column sum is a maximum, then this person can receive a message from everybody in one or two steps. In our example, columns 1, 3, and 4 all have maximal column sum 2, and hence all three of these men can be reached by any man in one or two steps.

These results do not appear very surprising when there are only four men in our network; but when we consider a complex network of a hundred people, they may be very useful indeed. For example, an efficiency expert studying a large firm may find a communication matrix a convenient means for representing either the communication system or the table of organization of the company. Should he find that the company forms a complete communication network, he could immediately search for the hub of command from which instructions can be given in one or two steps to any employee. And even if the network is incomplete, studying powers of the communication matrix would provide valuable information.

This example illustrates in very simple terms how numerical tools may be introduced in a problem where no numbers are apparent. Our final model will show how geometrical tools may sometimes be useful in a problem that at first appears completely nongeometrical.

Model No. 4

The problem confronting us deals with the ranking of a set of objects. Suppose that ten experts are each asked to rank a set of 50 objects, in order of preference. To allow a maximum amount of freedom, we will allow ties in the rankings. We are then supposed to arrive at a consensus ranking. How are we to do this? This problem can be reduced to a problem analogous to classical statistics problems[4] if we are able to introduce a measure of distance between rankings. So our problem is that of taking the set of all possible rankings of 50 objects and of turning them into a geometrical space, one in which a definite distance is defined between any two rankings. I will here summarize the results of some as yet unpublished research.[5]

Let us agree on some notation. We will have in mind a fixed number of objects to be ranked. We will denote by capital letters, *A, B, C*, etc., possible rankings. For example, if we have three objects, *a, b,* and *c,* in mind, then A may be the ranking where *b* is first, *a* is second, and *c* is third; and *B* may be the ranking where *c* is first and *a* and *b* are tied for second place. We want to introduce a measure of distance between pairs *A* and *B*, which will be denoted by $d(A,B)$. Let us try to agree on certain conditions that such a definition must satisfy.

Condition 1. d must satisfy the conditions for a distance laid down by a geometer. That is:

(1) $d(A, B) \geqq 0$, and equality holds if, and only if, A and B are the same ranking.
(2) $d(A, B) = d(B, A)$.
(3) $d(A, B) + d(B, C) \geqq d(A, C)$, and the equality holds if, and only if, the ranking B is between A and C.

For the last part of condition 1, we need a definition of "betweenness." We will define betweenness in terms of pairwise judgments—that is, we will say that ranking B is *between* A and C if for each pair of objects, i and j, the judgment of B is between that of A and C. In other words, for the given pair the judgment of B either agrees with A or agrees with C, or prefers i, C prefers j, and B declares them to be tied.

Next we must assure that our measure of distance does not in any way depend on the particular objects we have chosen for our rankings.

Condition 2. The definition of the distance d should not be affected by a relabeling of the set of objects to be ranked.

This means, for example, that if A rates three objects in the order a, b, c, and B rates them in the order c, b, a, the distance between these two rankings should be the same as the distance between the ranking b, c, a and a, c, b, since the latter may be obtained from the former by changing a to b, b to c, and c to a.

Condition 3. If the two rankings are in complete agreement at the beginning of the list and at the end of the list, and differ only as to the ranking of k objects in the middle, then this distance is the same as if these k objects were the only objects under consideration.

This condition is self-explanatory. Our final condition is in the nature of a convention. It may be thought of as choosing a unit of measurement.

Condition 4. The minimum positive distance is 1.

Let us suppose that we have agreed that these are four reasonable conditions for the definition of a distance between rankings. We have then translated our scientific problem into a purely mathematical problem. We can ask a mathematician three questions: (1) Is there any distance that will satisfy all of these conditions? Or, in other words, are our conditions consistent? (2) How can we characterize all definitions that will satisfy these four conditions? (3) What additional assumptions can we make that would narrow the possible choice from many distances to one?

In this particular case we are confronted with a pleasant surprise, in that we find that our conditions are indeed consistent, and that there is one and only one possible definition of distance which will satisfy all of these conditions. Therefore, if we have agreed on the four conditions above, we must agree that this is *the* correct definition of a distance. The details of this proof are here omitted.

The resulting distance may be described as follows. Compare the rankings A and B for each pair of individuals i and j. If the two rankings agree, we write down 0. If one prefers i to j and the other j to i, we write down 2. And if one expresses a preference while the other indicates a tie, we write down 1. Once we have these numbers written down for all pairs i and j, $d(A, B)$ equals the sum of these numbers.

Had we written down this definition to start with, we might have thought it a fairly reasonable way to measure the distance between two rankings. However, had other equally reasonable-sounding definitions been suggested, we would have had no rational way of choosing among them. With our present procedure the argument is reduced to the four conditions stated above. Anyone who accepts those four conditions *must* accept the resulting definition of d. Hence, anyone who rejects our definition of a distance must specify which of our conditions he rejects, and should be forced to give conditions of his own which are reasonable and which lead to a unique choice of the distance function. In this way an argument about a sociological problem can be put on a useful plane.

As an illustration, we show in Figure 4 the possible rankings of three objects and the distances between these rankings. The notation used is such that $\left\{\begin{matrix} a \\ b\text{-}c \end{matrix}\right\}$ indicates that a is in first place, b and c are tied for second place. Distances between neighboring rankings are indicated in the figure. Thus, e.g., the (shortest) distance between $\left\{\begin{matrix} a \\ b \\ c \end{matrix}\right\}$ and $(a\text{-}b\text{-}c)$ is $1 + 2 = 3$.

If we now ask a number of experts to rank three objects, we may use Figure 4 to find the consensus ranking. This ranking may be defined as the one such that the sum of its distances from the various

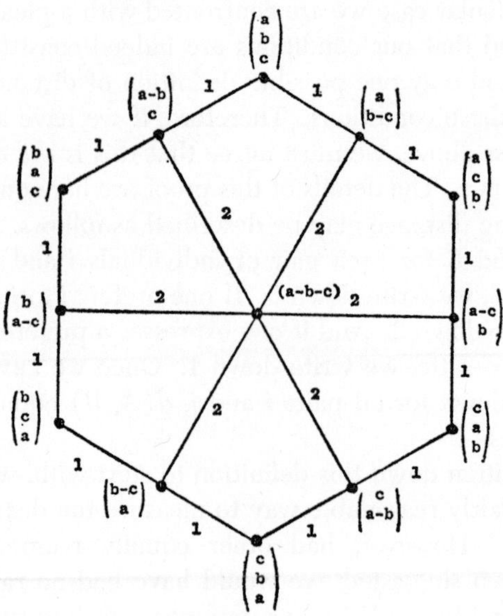

Figure 4

experts' rankings should be a minimum. Alternatively, it is sometimes convenient to take the sum of the squares of the distances to be a minimum. This would mean, for example, that if we have three experts, two of whom hand in the ranking, *a, b, c,* and one the ranking *b, a, c,* then the method of minimizing the sums of the distances will give *a, b, c* as the consensus ranking, while the method of minimizing the sum of squares of distances will yield a tie between *a* and *b,* with *c* a definite third. On the other hand, if there is considerable disagreement among the three experts—if, for example, the first one rates *a, b, c* in that order; the second one *b, c, a;* and the third one *c, a, b*—then the method of minimizing the sums of the squares of the distances will tell us that the consensus ranking is a three-way tie. The method of minimizing the sums of the distances, on the other hand, will give us three possible consensus rankings, namely, the three rankings given by the individual judges.

It is an essential feature of either of these methods that it always yields us at least one possible consensus ranking; but, as illustrated above, it may yield us more than one consensus. These basic tools enable one to carry out a certain amount of statistical work on rankings by experts.

An interesting question to consider is the relation between this definition of distance and the selection of consensus rankings on the one hand, and the work of K. J. Arrow on the other hand.

Arrow considered conditions that any reasonable system of social choice must satisfy.[6] His major result may be stated, in our terminology, as follows: *There is no method of selecting a consensus ranking from arbitrary sets of individual rankings that satisfies all his conditions.*

We have proposed two different ways of arriving at a consensus ranking, and hence we must ask how our methods escaped from the Arrow theorem. We find, first of all, that we have violated one of his basic conditions. This is the "condition of irrelevant alternatives," which has frequently been criticized. One consequence of this condition is the following: If we have three individuals ranking our objects, and if we know that two have ranked *a* ahead of *b* while the third has ranked *b* ahead of *a*, then we should be able to tell how *a* and *b* are ranked (relative to each other) by the consensus ranking.

However, if we have two ranking $\left\{\begin{matrix} a \\ c \\ b \end{matrix}\right\}$ and one $\left\{\begin{matrix} b \\ a \\ c \end{matrix}\right\}$, our consensus ranking by either method will be $\left\{\begin{matrix} a \\ b\text{-}c \end{matrix}\right\}$. While if two individuals arrive at the ranking $\left\{\begin{matrix} a \\ b \\ c \end{matrix}\right\}$ and the third at $\left\{\begin{matrix} b \\ c \\ a \end{matrix}\right\}$, then the consensus will be $\left\{\begin{matrix} a\text{-}b \\ c \end{matrix}\right\}$. In the former case *a* is preferred to *b* by the consensus, while in the latter they are tied. When we examine these two situations on Figure 4, they appear exactly alike, and it is hard to see why anyone would disagree with the consensus rankings. This lends further evidence to the thesis that the condition of irrelevant alternatives should be rejected.

But there is a second and more basic way in which our methods differ from those investigated by Arrow, namely, that we occasionally arrive at multiple consensus rankings. We conclude that the requirement of a unique social ordering is too restrictive. It suffices that we should arrive at a unique ordering "in most cases."

Conclusion

The four models discussed above illustrate various ways in which mathematics may be useful in nonnumerical and nonspatial problems in the social sciences. They illustrate how both modern algebra and modern geometry provide new techniques for these fields, and they show that these techniques may apply in situations where numbers and space are never introduced or where numbers and space are more or less artificially introduced into nonmathematical problems.

Of particular importance is the method illustrated in the fourth model. Often social scientists may be in agreement on requirements for the solution of a certain problem, even when no agreement can be reached on an actual solution. In such cases a mathematician should be consulted. He may show them that it is impossible to meet all the requirements they have laid down, and in that case they would have to agree on ways of asking for less. Or, very likely, he may tell them that there are infinitely many ways of solving their problem, and give them some indication of the kind of additional requirements they could make on a solution. Finally in an ideal situation such as the one illustrated in Model 4, he may be able to prove that there is a unique solution to the problem they have laid down. In this case he would solve, once and for all, a hitherto unresolved problem, and would provide the social scientist with a most useful tool for his work.

NOTES

1. The graph model is from D. Cartwright and F. Harary, "Structural Balance: A Generalization of Heider's Theory," *Psycho. Rev.*, 1956, *5*: 277–293.
2. An improved treatment of the same model may be found in J. G. Kemeny, J. L. Snell, and G. L. Thompson, *Introduction to Finite Mathematics,* Englewood Cliffs, N.J.: Prentice-Hall, 1957. See Chapter VII, Sections 7 and 8.
3. This theorem is proved in Kemeny, Snell, and Thompson, *op. cit.* See Chapter VII, Section 2.

4. See J. G. Kemeny, "Generalized Random Variables," *Pacif. J.*, in press.
5. To be published in J. G. Kemeny and J. L. Snell, *Mathematical Models in the Social Sciences,* Boston: Ginn, in press.
6. See K. J. Arrow, *Social Choice and Individual Values,* New York: Wiley, 1951.

Quality and Quantity in Quantum Physics

VICTOR F. WEISSKOPF

I

IN THIS ESSAY the antithesis Quality versus Quantity is understood to be related to the contrast between the specific and the unspecific, between individuality and continuous change, or between well-defined patterns and unordered flow. In this sense quality and quantity play a fundamental role in the basic concepts of quantum physics and in our scientific picture of the natural world. Of necessity our presentation of the role of this antithesis will be somewhat short and sketchy, and it can be justified only by the fact that not enough attempts are made by physicists to elucidate the basic ideas of the quantum theory, a field of human thought that, more than any other scientific achievement, has deepened and broadened our understanding of the world in which we live.

A case in point is the history of ideas on the structure of the planetary system. Let us consider three phases of this history: the ancient Pythagorean ideas; the modern ideas based on Newton's theory of gravity; and our present ideas regarding another planetary system—the system of electrons revolving around the atomic nucleus, the atom.

We are not interested here in the details of the Pythagorean system of heavenly bodies (e.g., the question as to which is the center and which moves in circles around the center), but in only one feature: the fundamental importance the Pythagoreans attributed to the numerical ratios of the radii of the orbits and to the numerical ratios of the periods of revolution of the different heavenly bodies. They considered the simple numerical relations between these data as the essence of their system. According to their ideas these relations were the embodiment of the "harmony of the spheres"; they represented the inherent symmetry of the heavenly world as contrasted to the earthly. The harmonious interplay of the various celestial motions produced a music whose chords were audible to the intellectual ear and were a manifestation of the divine order of the universe. Thus not only the general structure of the solar system, but also the specific shapes and the actual periods of the orbits themselves were significant and uniquely predetermined. Any deviation would have disturbed the harmony of the spheres and therefore was unthinkable.

This picture of the solar system did not survive the development of a better understanding of the underlying facts. Isaac Newton recognized that the phenomenon of gravitational attraction was the guiding principle by which the motions of the planets would be fully understood. This discovery was the end product of a development that led to a complete change in the attitude toward the problem of planetary motion. Not only did it become obvious that the sun was the center of the system, but it was also recognized that the motions of the planets were governed by the same laws as governed terrestrial phenomena. For our purposes here, the following is important: The laws of gravity admit of many ways a planet might circle around the sun; it can be any orbit of elliptical shape. The specific orbits in which our planets actually are found cannot be determined by the fundamental law of motion, but by so-called "initial conditions," those prevailing when the system was being formed. In this sense the actual shapes are accidental. Slightly varying conditions at the beginning would have produced different orbits. We now have good reason to believe that there are many other solar systems among the stars whose planets have orbits quite different from those in our own system.

Here we have a characteristic trait of physical thinking up to the advent of quantum physics, a period generally referred to as that of "classical" physics. The fundamental laws determine only the general character of the phenomenon; they admit of a continuous variety of realizations. The phenomena actually realized depend upon influences acting before the phenomenon was allowed to develop without further interference from outside. For example, if another star swept close by our solar system, the planetary orbits would undergo a thorough change and would be quite different after the star had left; similarly, if another planetary system with a star like our sun and planets of the same masses as ours existed, it would be highly unlikely that its orbits would bear any resemblance to the orbits of our own system, except that the orbits also would be ellipses and that their time of revolution would be the same function of the size of the ellipse.

It is typical of classical physics up to the turn of the century that its laws predetermine only the general character of the phenomena. The exact course of events can be predicted from the laws only if the situation at some past time is exactly known. The laws tell us only how an event develops; they do not tell us why we have this "solution of the equation" rather than another which would equally well fit the laws. This choice is considered accidental.

Since the time of Newton, classical physics has developed with the usual scientific crescendo and with ever increasing success, not only in mechanics but also by encompassing many different phenomena such as electricity and heat. The laws of nature discovered in this development were extremely successful in describing the character of many diverse phenomena. Hence these laws had to be a part of the real structure of the world around us. However, around the turn of the century it become obvious that the world of classical physics lacked some essential features to be found in the actual world. The stage was set for new discoveries.

II

To illustrate the situation at the beginning of quantum physics, let us return to a planetary system analogous to that of the sun and its planets—that of the atom. The properties of the solar system were exhaustively understood through the application of the laws of classical mechanics. The experiments of Rutherford and his contemporaries have shown that there exists another similar system, the system of electrons in the atom. It consists of electrons circling round an atomic nucleus, just as the planets revolve round the sun. The attractive force replacing gravity is the electric attraction between the negatively charged electrons and the positively charged nucleus. This force should produce the same type of motion in both cases, since it displays one important characteristic: it decreases as the reciprocal square of the distance.

The predictions on the basis of the atomic model were fulfilled in many respects. For example, the time of revolution of the electrons (which can be deduced from the frequency of the light emitted by the atoms) is just about what one would expect from the size of the orbits (as deduced from the atom dimensions). However, the atom has some very important properties one would never expect in a planetary system—the most striking, the *identity* of the atoms of a given material. One must be impressed by the fact that pure materials show identical properties, no matter where they come from or what their previous history has been. Two pieces of gold, mined at two different locations and treated in very different ways, cannot be distinguished from one another. All the properties of each individual gold atom are fixed and completely independent of its previous history.

The identity of individual atoms is strikingly not in keeping with what is expected from a mechanical system, particularly one like the planetary system. The particular shape and size of the orbits are expected to depend markedly upon the past history of the system; it would be extremely improbable to find two atoms with exactly the same size and shape. The difficulty becomes obvious when we consider a gas such as air: the atoms in air collide many million times per second. According to classical mechanics, each of these collisions would thoroughly change the orbits of the electrons. In fact, however, the atoms emerge completely restored to their original form after each collision.

The problem of definite shapes in atomic phenomena versus the arbitrarily changing forms in classical mechanics permeates atomic physics. We find definite "qualities" in the atomic world where we expected quantitative differences. The crystal structure of matter reveals well-defined simple geometrical patterns in the atomic structure that ought to be absent in classical mechanics. Nature exhibits all around us characteristic and specific properties of various materials, which, in spite of their overwhelming variety, are always reproducible and recurrent. The specificity of material qualities in nature is in need of a fundamental explanation.

Even the existence of elementary particles such as electrons, protons, neutrons needs some better understanding. The particles are the building stones of the atoms and must *a fortiori* exhibit complete identity among members of one kind if the atoms of a given type prove to be identical. Within the framework of classical physics it is hard to understand why there should not exist electrons with slightly less charge, or with a different mass, or with a spin (rotation about an axis) somewhat at variance with the spin of the observed electron. It is the existence of well-defined specific qualities, in which nature abounds, that runs counter to the spirit of classical physics.

In this connection one must mention the Boltzmann paradox, although the fundamental significance of this point might escape the nonphysicist. There seems to be no end to the following regression: matter consists of atoms; atoms of electrons and nuclei; nuclei of protons and neutrons; electrons, protons, and neutrons of . . . . Of itself, the existence of this regression should not worry us; it serves as a constant challenge to further research. However, in 1890 Boltzmann pointed out that on the basis of classical mechanics one is led to expect that for a system of atoms in thermal equilibrium at a given temperature, the thermal energy should be divided among all the modes of motion. This leads to a puzzle: all possible motions should share in the heat motion; in a piece of heated material the electrons should run around faster; the protons should vibrate more strongly within the nuclei; the parts of which the protons are made should move faster within their bounds; etc. Hence the abovementioned regression would unavoidably lead to an infinite *sink* of heat energy, and it would need immense energies to heat the smallest part of matter. Here, as before, the classically admissible modes of motion are obviously too unspecific and too varied, and do not explain the structure of matter.

One main feature of classical physics is the divisibility of each process. Every physical process can be thought of as consisting of a succession of partial processes. Theoretically at least, each process can be followed step by step in time and space. The orbit of an electron round the nucleus may be thought of as a succession of small displacements. The electron of a given charge may be thought of as consisting of parts of a smaller charge. This is the point to be discarded if one wants to understand what we see in nature: quality, specificity, and individuality.

III

The great step forward that solved the paradoxes here outlined was achieved within only thirteen years, from the discovery of the quantum orbits of the atom by Bohr in 1913 to the final development of quantum mechanics by Bohr, Heisenberg, Schrödinger, and Dirac in 1926. The idea of the quantum of action, however, had already been conceived in 1900 by Max Planck. There is hardly any period in the history of science in which so much has been clarified by so few in so short a period.

The study of the properties of atoms has led to many indications of new phenomena outside the scope of classical physics. The most striking is the particle and wave duality. In classical physics a beam of light and a beam of electrons are fundamentally different. The former is a bundle of electromagnetic waves propagating through space in a certain direction; no material is moving; only the state of the electromagnetic field in space is changing. In contrast, a beam of particles consists of actual matter in small units moving straight forward; it is as different as is the motion of waves on a lake from that of a school of fish swimming in the same direction. All the greater was the surprise of the physicists when electron beams were found to exhibit wave properties, and light beams to exhibit particle behavior.

The particle nature of light is revealed by the fact that the energy or the momentum of the beam is transferred to matter in finite amounts—the so-called light quanta. The size of the energy quanta is proportional to the frequency f; it has the value hf, where h is Planck's constant. The existence of the smallest package of energy hf turns out to be a general property of any vibrating process.

The wave nature of particle beams manifests itself in many ways. One is the well-known observation that particle beams show the same kind of "interference" as wave beams. A beam that penetrates a screen through two slits shows the characteristic intensity patterns, which are quite different from the simple sum of intensities expected of two separate beams emerging from the slits on the basis of the classical picture of particles. The pattern of intensity is in fact the same as if obtained from a wave passing through two slits. Another perhaps somewhat indirect manifestation is found in the atom itself.

In many respects the electron orbits have shown a striking similarity to vibrating sound waves restricted within the confines of the atom. In fact, this aspect already provides some of the essential features missing in the classical picture. For example, a standing wave confined to a finite volume can assume only a certain restricted number of shapes, in particular when its frequency is supposed to be low, as it must be for the states of lowest energy according to Planck's law. These shapes are well defined and have a simple symmetrical structure, a fact known from other examples of standing waves, for example, those in a violin string or in the air column of an organ pipe. They also have the property of "regeneration"; when a perturbing effect has changed the shape, they assume their original shape after the perturbation is over.

The main question now is: How can a particle in motion exhibit any wave nature? How is it possible that an electron is partly a particle and partly a wave? After all, a careful tracing of the electron along its motion must decide this question and put it in either one or the other category. Here we come to the question of the divisibility of atomic phenomena. Can we really perform this tracing? There are technical problems in the way. If we want to "look" at the detailed structure of the orbit, we must use light waves with a very small wave length. Such light, however, has a high frequency, hence a big energy quantum. When it hits the electron it will knock it out of the orbit and destroy the very object of our examination. These considerations are the basis of Heisenberg's uncertainty relations. They express the negative statement that certain physical measurements are impossible. Characteristically, just those measurements which would decide between the wave or the particle nature of the electron (or proton, or any other entity) are impossible. If one performs these measurements, the subject has thoroughly changed its state by the very act of performance.

Here we recognize the highly important fact that this impossibility of certain measurements is more than a mere technical limitation that some day might be overcome by clever instrumentation. If it were possible to perform such measurements, the coexistence of wave and particle properties in a single object would collapse, since these measurements would prove one of the two alternatives to be wrong. However, we know from a great wealth of observations that our objects exhibit both wave and particle properties. Hence the Heisenberg restrictions must have a deeper root: they are a necessary corollary of the dual nature of atomic objects. If they were broken, our interpretation of the wide field of atomic phenomena would be nothing but a web of errors and its amazing success would be based upon accidental coincidences.

Atomic phenomena present us with a much richer reality than we are accustomed to face in classical macroscopic physics. The response of the object to our experimentation displays features that do not occur with single objects in our macroscopic experiences. Hence our description of the object cannot be as "detached" from the observing process as before. We can describe atomic reality only by telling truthfully what happens when we observe a phenomenon in different ways, although it seems incredible to the noninitiated that so many things should happen to one given object.

The wave nature of the electron in the atom is connected with the indivisibility, the wholeness, of the state of the atom. If we force a subdivision of the process and try to "see" more accurately where the electron "really" is within this wave, we find it there as a real particle, but we have destroyed the subtle individuality of the "quantum state." It is the wave nature, however, which gives rise to the characteristic properties of the quantum state—its simple shape, the regeneration of the original form after perturbation, in short, the specific qualities of the atom. The great discovery of quantum physics is the existence of these individual quantum states, each of which forms an indivisible whole, as long as they are not attacked by penetrating means of observation. Any attempt to observe subdivisions uses means of such high energy that they destroy the delicate structure of the quantum state.

The same situation exists also with the previously discussed electron beam which passes through a pair of slits in a screen and exhibits interference phenomena afterward. This phenomenon also has its individuality, its wholeness. When one tries to arrange a follow-up experiment in order to find out through which hole the electron went, the interference phenomenon is gone. The follow-up is too severe an operation; it destroys the wholeness of the quantum phenomenon.

At this stage of our discussion it will appear quite natural that predictions of atomic phenomena sometimes must remain probability predictions only. The prediction of the exact spot where the electron will be found after destroying a quantum state with high-energy light is a case of this kind. The quantum state is an individual entity which cannot be divided into parts without destroying it, although it spreads out over a finite region in space. If the quantum state is looked at with pin-pointing light, the electron will be found somewhere in the region of the wave, the exact point being undefined.

We now can return to the cause of identity among the same kind of atoms, and of their characteristic properties. The kind and shape of a standing electron wave are fixed and given when confined by the electric attraction of the nucleus, as is the shape of the vibration of a violin string. The standing wave of lowest frequency is spherically symmetrical, the next higher one has a "figure eight" symmetry; each step has its well-defined shape. These are the fundamental forms of which atomic structure is built. Even if we destroy an atom by removing an electron and later try to build it up again, the electron will return to the same quantum state from which it previously had been removed. There exists only one unique state of lowest energy for each kind of atom. This is in complete contradistinction to the situation in a classical planetary system.

We are reminded of the Pythagorean "pre-established harmony"; the atomic quantum states have specific shapes and frequencies which are uniquely predetermined. Every hydrogen atom in the world strikes the same chord of frequencies, as given by the Balmer formula of spectral terms. Here we find the "harmony of the spheres" rediscovered in the atomic world, but this time clearly understood as a vibration phenomenon of confined electron waves. The complete identity of two gold atoms comes from the fact that the same number of electrons are confined by the same electric charge in the center and therefore produce the same wave vibrations.

It is often said that the atomic world is less "real" than the visible world around us because of the fact that we cannot describe the atomic phenomena independently of the mode of observation, and because of the fact that one uses dual descriptions which cannot be visualized in any simple way or calculated without the use of abstract mathematics. Heisenberg says:

The conception of the objective reality of the elementary particles has thus evaporated in a curious way, not into the fog of some new, obscure, or not yet understood reality concept, but into the transparent clarity of a mathematics that represents no longer the behavior of the elementary particles but rather our knowledge of this behavior.*

We do not agree with the claim that there is any lack of reality in the atomic world. After all, the visible real world consists of the same atoms that exhibit this strange behavior. It is true that the atomic world differs from our accustomed world more than anyone had expected; it has much richer patterns of phenomena than we can visualize with classical concepts. But all this does not make it less real. It is not very meaningful to distinguish between the actual behavior of the elementary particles and our knowledge of this behavior. It is precisely the ever growing insight into the detailed workings of nature which gives us confidence in having discovered something about the real world.

IV

The individuality and the stability of the quantum states have definite limitations. The atom has a unique and specific shape only as long as it is not disturbed by outside effects strong enough for an excitation of higher quantum states. Under very energetic interference from outside, the individuality of the quantum effects disappears completely and the system acquires the classical continuous character (often referred to as the correspondence principle). Hence the quantum character of mechanical systems is limited; it is exhibited only as long as the disturbing factors are weaker than the excitation energy to higher quantum states. This excitation threshold depends on the character of the system. It is always higher, the smaller the spatial dimension of the system. For example, it needs very little energy to change the quantum state of a large molecule; it needs much more to change the quantum state of an atom; and it needs many thousand times more energy to produce a change within the atomic nucleus. We arrive at a characteristic sequence of conditions which we may call the "quantum ladder."

At very low temperature, the molecules of every substance form

* Werner Heisenberg, "The Representation of Nature in Contemporary Physics," *Dædalus, 1958, 87:* 100.

one big unit, a tightly bound crystal, in which one part is identical to any other. If we warm it to a higher temperature, melting or evaporation sets in and liquids or gases result. In a gas such as air at normal temperature, each molecule moves for itself in differing paths, bouncing against one another in irregular motion. The motions of the molecules are no longer alike; they are constantly changing, and they correspond to what we expect on the basis of classical mechanics. The molecules themselves, however, are still identical, one to the other. They interact as do inert billiard balls. The collision energies are not high enough to destroy their quantum state.

At still higher temperatures, the energy of collision surpasses the excitation energies of the molecules. The internal motion of the atoms and electrons participates in the exchange of energy. This is the temperature at which the gas begins to glow and emit light. If still more energy is supplied, the molecules split into atoms, and further on the electrons are torn off the atoms. Then the atoms lose their individuality and specificity. Electrons and atomic nuclei move freely and in random fashion; no two electrons move exactly alike. This state of affairs occurs at temperatures as high as exist in the interior of stars. It is possible, however, to create similar conditions in the laboratory for a small number of atoms. At those energies the atomic nuclei are still in their ground states. They are still identical and specific, whereas the atoms are already reduced from their specific qualities to unspecific random behavior.* Only if the energies of millions of electron volts are fed into the system, as is done in our big particle accelerators, are the higher quantum states of the nucleus excited or the nucleus even disintegrated into its constituents, the protons and the neutrons. Once this is done, the nucleus also has lost its quality and its specific properties, and has become a classical gas of protons and neutrons.

The newest giant accelerators are about to pour so much energy into the protons and neutrons themselves that the latter will begin to show internal structure and differentiation, and thus lose their

* There is here a danger of confusion in our terminology: the word "quantum" is not related to what we understand by "quantity" versus quality. The term "quantum state" applies to the peculiar individual states of motion in atoms, molecules, or nuclei, which are the basis of the specificity and *quality* of these objects.

innate identity. This development may advance toward new and unknown structures if the energy is further increased—or it may stop at some point, without yielding any new particles. We do not know and probably will never know unless we try it out.

The quantum ladder has made it possible to discover step by step the structure of the natural world. When we investigate phenomena at atomic energies, we need not worry about the internal structure of the nuclei; and when we study the mechanics of gases at normal temperatures, we need not worry about the internal structure of the atoms. In the former case we can consider the nuclei as identical unchangeable units—that is, as elementary particles; in the latter case each atom may be considered as such. Thus the observed phenomena are simpler and they can be understood without any knowledge of the internal structure of the constituents as long as the prevailing energies are so low that the constituents can be considered as inert units.

The phenomenon of the quantum ladder solves the Boltzmann paradox. The finer structure of matter does not participate in the exchange of energy until the average energy has reached the level of its quantum excitation. Hence only those types of motion whose energies can be excited at the prevailing temperatures participate in the heat exchange.

Let us now descend the quantum ladder, starting at the highest step known today. This may be a gas of protons, neutrons, and electrons at extremely high temperatures, with kinetic energies of many million electron volts. Not much individuality can be found under these conditions, except for the three elementary particles. Their motion is random and hence without any special order. At lower temperatures, say with kinetic energies of less than a million electron volts, the protons and neutrons assemble and form atomic nuclei. Much more specificity now enters into the picture. There are many possible atomic nuclei, the nuclei of the ninety-two elements and their isotopes, each a well-defined individual state. However, the motion of the electrons and the atomic nuclei is still at random, unordered, and continually changing. At still lower temperatures, corresponding to energies of a few volts only—this is the energy corresponding to the temperature of the surface of the sun (12,000 degrees F.)—electrons have fallen into regular quantum states around the atomic nuclei; this is the point on the quantum ladder at which the atoms with their specific individualities and chemical qualities appear. If we descend further, to the region of a tenth of an electron volt (about a few thousand degrees F.), we see that atoms can form simple molecules, and we find a much greater variety of chemical compounds, as distinct and specific as atoms, only somewhat less stable.

A further lowering of energy to a few hundredths of an electron volt (room temperature) brings us to a region where most molecules aggregate to liquids and crystals, thus adding to the diversity of matter. It is also the region in which giant chain molecules are formed. We have opened a completely new chapter of material specificity: living organisms. It starts with the formation of a great variety of chemical compounds of carbon with hydrogen, oxygen, and nitrogen—such as nucleic acids, amino acids, and proteins. The detailed dynamics of these giant molecules are not yet well understood, but some of their properties are well known. The most striking is the ability to include the formation of its replicas by combining simpler molecules into the pattern of the macromolecule itself.

The possibility of reproduction brings about a new mechanism: the structure most suited to reproduction, the one best protected against damage, will reproduce itself most abundantly. Hence we get a chain development of structures, the living organisms, which become consecutively better adapted according to the mechanism of natural selection. The reproduction of living structures is determined and guided by certain large molecules, of which the most important is DNA (desoxyribo nucleic acid). The internal structure of DNA (in particular the order in which the purine and pyrimidine bases are arranged in it) is the determining factor for the properties of the units which are constantly reproduced in the cycle of life. Hence it is again the individuality of quantum states which is responsible for specificity in life. The specific structure of the nucleic-acid bases and the stability of the order in which they are arranged in DNA form another example, albeit a complicated one, of unique and identical quantum states. Because of the large size of the molecules, the number of possible quantum states is enormously greater than in the case of simple atoms or molecules, and their forms are much more intricate and complicated. This is reflected by the great variety of living species.

The existence of life requires that the temperature must be low enough to allow the formation of the macromolecules, but it also requires temperatures high enough for the supply of energy necessary for life processes. If we proceed downward on our quantum ladder to zero temperature, life decays, and all matter forms a big crystal in which many of the existing varieties are preserved but are frozen into inactivity. Everything is then found in its lowest state, a state of high specificity but without any change or motion. This is the stage of death.

Very probably the development of matter in the history of the universe has descended the quantum ladder just as we have described it, from high to low energies, adding new quality with each step. The history of the material world as we see it immediately around us probably began in some accumulation of protons, neutrons, and electrons of very high energy, compressed by forces of gravity, within a young star. This was a period of little differentiation. Later on, the elementary particles aggregated to atom nuclei, and in the colder regions of the star atoms were formed. This was the first step toward quality and organization. Individual properties began to appear, motion and radiation were no longer all uniform. Classes of identical objects were created—one could distinguish one thing from another.

On the surface of stars and the colder planets, the temperature further decreased, and conditions suitable for the formation of a great variety of chemical compounds were established. At that stage the world acquired an aspect not unknown to us, one of rocks, deserts, and waters, abundant in minerals and chemicals but without any form of life. Finally, at certain places in the universe where conditions were favorable, the great adventure of nature took place of which we ourselves are a part. The organic macromolecules began their cycles of reproduction, and evolution toward the varied forms of life appeared. The development from quantity to quality then reached that stage of diversity and abundance which we know as the world in which we live. Human life, men's thought, and men's feelings are but one manifestation of this stage.

The contrast with the formless chaos of the beginning vividly illustrates the innate trend of matter toward distinction and specificity, a trend ultimately based upon the stability and individuality of quantum states. We who are living in the twentieth century are privileged to witness the most exciting phase of this development: the moment when nature in its human form begins to recognize a few of its own essential features.

The Quantification of Sensation

S. S. Stevens

Imagine that your finger is resting on the button of an electromagnetic vibrator and that a pair of earphones is clamped to your ears. Now you are asked to adjust the loudness in your ears by varying a gain control in order to make the sound from the earphones seem as strong as the vibration on your finger. Very probably you will say that this request makes no particular sense. In this type of experiment—the latest step in the century-old struggle to understand the dynamics of the sensory mechanisms—the observer often claims at the outset that, in "quality" at least, the sound cannot really match the vibration.

Nevertheless, once a person undertakes to make the two sensations as equal as possible in apparent strength—in "quantity" as it were—he finds it surprisingly easy to decide on a degree of loudness that seems to match a particular vibration on his finger; and when the stimulus on the finger is made more intense, he readily finds a matching loudness of appropriately increased magnitude. The orderly manner in which observers have performed the task of cross-modality matching has disclosed some beautifully simple laws of sensory action. The present account is concerned with these quantitative laws.

We employ the marvelous transducers known as sense organs in order to appraise the state of the environment and ascertain its objective condition. We see the turn in the road ahead, hear the spoken word, feel the coin in the pocket. Eyes and ears and fingers, like radio sets, are versatile sources of information which most of us enjoy with seldom a thought about their internal workings. Yet these sensory transducers, like radio sets, have specific input-output relations (operating characteristics), and the problem of their operation is quite as profound as any biological puzzle confronting us. No man-made device quite duplicates the eye with its acute sensitivity to faint light. In order to evoke a visual sensation, only a couple of quanta of light may be all that is needed at the retina. Along with this delicate threshold goes a capacity to respond to stimuli over a dynamic range that is greater than a trillion to one. No less startling is the performance of the ear, an elaborate mechanical system that somehow manages to set off a sensation of hearing when the eardrum is moved by a sound wave through a displacement smaller than the diameter of the smallest molecule. Here too an incredible sensitivity is combined with an ability to respond without ill effect to a thunderous roar containing trillions of times the threshold energy.

So wide is the range of operation of the eye and the ear that we commonly resort to logarithmic scales to describe their respective stimuli. The familiar decibel scale is one such device. On this scale, a difference of 10 decibels represents a tenfold increase in energy; 20 decibels, a hundredfold increase, etc. If we choose as

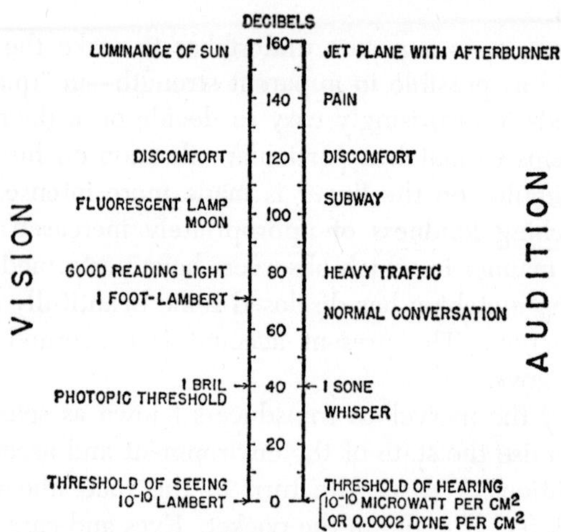

Figure 1

A decibel scale for light and sound, showing the approximate levels of luminance and sound intensity produced by various sources, together with a few important threshold levels. The points indicated by arrows are exact levels, fixed by definitions; the other levels are approximate only. The *bril* and the *sone* are subjective units of brightness and loudness, respectively.

reference levels a pair of values a little below the respective thresholds, we can set up a common decibel scale for light and sound in such a way that interesting similarities between the two senses become at once apparent. As illustrated in Figure 1, the physical luminance of the sun's disc stands about the same number of decibels above the human threshold as does the sound intensity near a jet airplane with an after-burner, which is probably the loudest sustained noise yet produced. Our sense organs can tolerate such levels of light and sound but briefly; these levels far exceed the point at which discomfort becomes pronounced, which for most people lies in the vicinity of 120 decibels. Curiously enough, the comfortable levels, both for seeing and for listening, lie near the middle of the decibel scale, and when stimuli grow fainter than about 40 decibels we strain to perceive them.

The decibel scale in Figure 1 stands for two physical scales, both contrived by operations familiar to the laboratory. The fact that two forms of energy (light and sound) can be scaled in such a way that similar sensory effects appear to emerge at related points along the common continuum suggests that, whatever the dependence of subjective brightness on physical luminance may be, a similar dependence must relate loudness to the energy of sound. An interesting conjecture, this—but is it true? How can the form of such a dependence be specified? Clearly, the rough tabulations on the chart in Figure 1 do not settle the matter, for at best they are merely suggestive. What is needed is some means of measuring the sensations involved.

Measurement

The eminent scholars who have said that sensation cannot be measured comprise a long and distinguished list. Some have asserted it flatly, as a truth too obvious for argument. Others have suggested reasons. The well-known claim of William James is perhaps the most quotable: "Our feeling of pink is surely not a portion of our feeling of scarlet; nor does the light of an electric arc seem to contain that of a tallow candle in itself."

That sentence was written some seventy years ago. The fact that sensations cannot be separated into component parts, or laid end to end like measuring sticks, was once a telling argument against their measurability. But that was before there was general recognition of the fact that measurement is not limited to counting. It was in fact before many scientists had become fully aware that mathematics with its number system is a game of signs and rules, man-made and arbitrary, like the game of chess. The formal emancipation of mathematics, its complete decoupling from matters of empirical, earthy fact, was destined to fashion a new outlook on the problem of measurement.

Our understanding of the profound difference between science and mathematics took many centuries to develop, mainly because the operations of both measurement and mathematics had seemed at first to be one and the same process. The earliest scales of measurement were schemes for the counting of goods and chattels, pebbles and beads, friends and enemies. The numbers themselves, with their rules of combination and all the paraphernalia that grew into modern mathematics, originated as a simple model invented to mirror what was done with collections of objects, to aid in the measurement of numerosity. Since arithmetic was invented to serve the purpose of measurement, it is not surprising that the isomorphic correspondence between certain arithmetical operations and the more elementary empirical operations of counting was tight and satisfying. It was, in fact, too much so, for man soon found himself a slave to his invention: the properties of the model began to dictate what was and what was not to be considered measurement. But with the ultimate decoupling of the formal, arbitrary, empty, gamelike aspects of mathematics from the empirical pursuits of the "concrete" disciplines it became clear that the province of measurement extends to wherever our ingenuity can contrive systematic rules for pinning numbers on things.

The number system is merely a model, to be used in whatever way we please. It is a rich model, to be sure, and one or another aspect of its syntax can often be made to portray one or another property of objects or events. It is a useful convention, therefore, to define as measurement the assigning of numbers to objects or events in accordance with a systematic rule. Since there are different kinds of rules, there are different kinds of measurement; but for each kind some degree of isomorphism obtains between the empirical relations among objects and the formal relations among numbers.

Among the empirical properties of the world for which numbers may serve as models the most important are these:

1. *Identity:* numbers may serve as names or labels to identify items or classes;
2. *Order:* numbers may serve to reflect the rank order of items;
3. *Intervals:* numbers may serve to reflect differences or distances among items;
4. *Ratios:* numbers may serve to reflect ratios among items.

Corresponding to each of these uses there is a type of scale: nominal, ordinal, interval, and ratio, as set forth in Table 1, along with definitions and examples. The key to the nature of these different scales lies in a powerful but simple principle: the concept of invariance. When we have carried out a set of empirical operations (such as comparisons, matchings, balancings, orderings, etc.) we assign a set of numbers to reflect the outcome of the operations. Then comes the crucial question: In what ways can we transform the numbers without loss of empirical information?

As shown in Table 1, each of the four scales has its characteristic group of permissible transformations. For our present purposes, the group of greatest interest is the one that defines the ratio scale, for this is the most useful type of scale. Here we can only multiply by a constant, as we do in converting inches to centimeters, or seconds to minutes. Any more radical transformation would distort the picture that the ratio scale serves to portray.

The measurement of sensation on the most interesting type of scale would call, therefore, for a procedure for assigning numbers to sensations in such a way that anything more drastic than multiplication by a constant would cause a loss of information. Such a scale would be a ratio scale, and with it we could tell how sensory magnitude grows with the stimulus input. The numbers on this scale would allow us to specify, for example, when one sensation is twice as intense as another.

Sensation

Since each of us can testify that sounds may rise or fall in loudness and that light may grow dim or bright, the problem of assessing the

TABLE 1

A Classification of Scales of Measurement

Measurement is the assignment of numbers to objects or events according to rule. The rules and the resulting kinds of scales are tabulated below. The basic operations needed to create a given scale are all those listed in the second column, down to and including the operation listed opposite the scale. The third column gives the mathematical transformations that leave the scale form invariant. Any number x on a scale can be replaced by another number x' where x' is the function of x listed in column 2. The fourth column lists, cumulatively downward, examples of statistics that show invariance under the transformations of column 3 (the mode, however, is invariant only for discrete variables). Reprinted, by permission, from Stevens, "Measurement and Man," *Science,* 1958, *127:* 383–389.

Scale	*Basic Empirical Operations*	*Mathematical Group-Structure*	*Permissible Statistics (Invariantive)*	*Typical Examples*
Nominal	Determination of equality	Permutation group $x' = f(x)$ where $f(x)$ means any one-to-one substitution	Number of cases Mode "Information" measures Contingency correlation	"Numbering" of football players Assignment of type or model numbers to classes
Ordinal	Determination of greater or less	Isotonic group $x' = f(x)$ where $f(x)$ means any increasing monotonic function	Median Percentiles Order correlation (type 0: interpreted as a test of order)	Hardness of minerals Grades of leather, lumber, wool, and so forth Intelligence-test raw scores

Interval	Determination of the equality of intervals or of differences	Linear or affine group $x' = ax + b$ $a > 0$	Mean Standard deviation Order correlation (type I: interpreted as r) Product moment (r)	Temperature (Fahrenheit and Celsius) Position on a line Calendar time Potential energy Intelligence-test "standard scores" (?)
Ratio	Determination of the equality of ratios	Similarity group $x' = cx$ $c > 0$	Geometric mean Harmonic mean Percent variation	Length, numerosity, density, work, time intervals, and so forth Temperature (Kelvin) Loudness (sones) Brightness (brils)

functions involved hardly seems forbidding. Nor need it be. Nevertheless, one can scarcely raise the question of measuring sensation without rousing a troop of old ghosts whose rustling and fluttering center chiefly around the issue of privacy. Ever since Descartes set mind apart from matter we have had to contend with the dualistic view that man's higher processes are a thing apart, inaccessible to science and measurement. However respectable quantification may prove to be in physical science, in psychology it still walks in the shadow of suspicion, for there lurks in many of us a feeling, not only that human experience is somehow inscrutable, but also that measurement, because of some unfeeling rigor, may bruise the human spirit if we go probing its inner reaches with the aid of scales and numbers.

Actually, however, in the study of sensation there need be no question of violating the privacy of immediate experience (whatever that may mean), because the sensation that science deals with is the type of human reaction that lends itself to public scrutiny. What is here meant by sensation is a construct, a conception built upon the objective operations of stimulation and reaction. We study the responses of organisms, not some nonphysical mental stuff that by definition defies objective test. Especially in the search for general sensory laws does it become obvious that the term *sensation* derives its meaning from the reactions, verbal or otherwise, made by organisms in response to stimuli. This operational principle, faithfully adhered to, seems the surest guide toward making quantitative order out of the reactions of sensory systems to the energetic configurations of the environment.

Quality versus Quantity

There is ready agreement among all observers that sensations come in so many and such varied forms as to elude complete description. All the richness of the daily sights and sounds and tastes and smells and feelings to which our sense organs admit us can no more be captured within a formula than can the intricate dancing of a falling leaf. Nevertheless, once a few basic distinctions are made, there emerge some simple and engaging principles that relate certain aspects of sensation to certain properties of the impinging forces of the environment. Perhaps the chief of these distinctions is the one between quantity and quality, or magnitude and kind, or size and sort. No pair of common words quite fits the distinction; but what it means concretely is that sweet is different from sour, although both may vary from strong to weak.

It is only fair to point out that psychophysics, the science of sensation, has little to say as yet about qualitative variations among sensations. This aspect of the sensory world confronts us with a succession of baffling and discontinuous leaps as we go from quality to quality, as well as from one sense modality to another—and no one quite knows why. The various colors, tastes, smells, and feelings seem not to lie on a continuum, but to exist in more or less complete independence of one another. In terms of the scales of measurement listed in Table 1, the sensory qualities provide a first-rate example of measurement at the nominal level—the most primitive type of measurement, where all we can do is identify and label. Sometimes a crude ordering seems possible, but for the most part the qualities are just what they are, and the best we can do is to name them.

Quite different opportunities present themselves for those aspects of sensation that appear to lie on a continuum of some sort. Here we can usually order sensations on a scale from faint to intense, or on some other dimension, and for many continua a form of measurement stronger than ordinal may readily be achieved. It would of course simplify the problem if a common set of rules governed all perceptual continua, but this turns out not to be the case. At least one basic distinction must be made between two kinds of continua.

The prototypes of the two kinds of continua are exemplified by loudness and pitch. Loudness is an aspect of sound that has about it what can best be described as degrees of magnitude or quantity. Pitch does not. Pitch varies from high to low; it has a kind of position, and in a sense it is a qualitative continuum. Loudness may be called a *prothetic* continuum, and pitch a *metathetic* one. The criteria that define these two classes of continua reside wholly in how they behave in psychophysical experiments, but the names themselves are suggested by the nature of the physiological processes that appear to underlie each of them.

Sensory discrimination may be mediated by two processes: the one additive, the other substitutive. Additional excitation may be added to an excitation already present, or new excitation may be substituted for excitation that has been removed. An observer can tell, for example, when a light pressure becomes a strong pressure at a given point on the arm, and he can also tell when the stimulus is moved from that point to another location. Different sets of general laws govern these two types of sensory discrimination.

The metathetic, positional, qualitative continua seem to concern *what* and *where* as opposed to *how much.* They include such things as pitch, apparent position, apparent inclination, and apparent proportion. Perhaps they also include visual saturation and visual hue—at least to whatever extent hue may be made to behave as a continuum. All in all, the metathetic continua do not seem to comprise a neat and orderly class of perceptual variables, and as yet they have not been very thoroughly explored.

The prothetic continua, on the other hand, have lately yielded rich rewards for the systematic efforts made to scale their magnitudes. Some two dozen continua have been examined, always with the same outcome: the sensation magnitude ψ grows as a power function of the stimulus magnitude ϕ. In terms of a formula.

$$\psi = k\phi^n$$

In this equation, the constant k depends on the units of measurement and is not very interesting; but the value of the exponent n may vary from one sensory continuum to another. As a matter of fact, perhaps the most interesting thing about a sensory continuum is (as we shall see) the value of the exponent n.

So rarely does it happen in psychological studies that a simple quantitative law can be shown to hold under many diverse circumstances, that the widespread invariance of the power law becomes a matter of significant interest. A law of this form seems to govern our reactions to light and sound, taste and smell, warmth and cold, vibration and shock—in fact, every continuum yet explored on which variations in intensity may be said to exist. As a general psychophysical law it provides a new aid to understanding and a new challenge to explanation.

Before we consider it further, a word is in order concerning the antecedent state of affairs.

The Older Psychophysics

G. T. Fechner, the father of psychophysics, had other ideas about the psychophysical law. Although he was aware of conjectures to the effect that the growth of sensation might be governed by a power law, he damned the notion from the start and fought stubbornly to the end for his famous and erroneous logarithmic law. So well did he contend, in fact, that for almost a century Fechner's logarithmic law ruled the textbooks and the thinking in psychology and physiology.

Fechner's law (beautifully simple though wholly wrong) will probably not be abandoned without a struggle on the part of many scientists. It is founded on the idea that sensation can be measured by counting its constituent units, thought by Fechner to be the just noticeable differences. The just noticeable difference between two stimuli—the resolving power, so to speak—usually turns out to be proportional to the stimulus magnitude itself. It follows from this, by an argument that need not detain us here, that the number of just noticeable differences (Fechner's scale of sensation) grows as the logarithm of the stimulus.

The Fechnerian attack on the problem of sensation was an assault from the rear, an indirect approach via resolving power, or least detectable differences. The idea that measurement must be reducible to counting still prevailed in Fechner's time, and the older psychophysics was looking for something to count. William James, of course, objected that a sensation is a unitary thing, not like a pile of blocks or a congeries of elements. Scarlet, as he said, is not a collection of pinks. True enough; but James should not have concluded therefrom that sensations have no magnitude.

The new psychophysics takes the stand that sensation is analogous to many other scientific constructs to which measurement is commonly applied. Consider temperature, for example. No one hopes to slice temperature into units that can be added or subtracted like measuring rods or counted like beans. We know the temperature of a body only through that body's behavior, which we note by studying the effects the body produces on other systems. It is much the same with sensation: the magnitude of an observer's sensation may be discovered by a systematic study of what the observer does in a controlled experiment in which he operates on other systems. He may, for instance, adjust the loudness in his ears to match the apparent intensity of various amplitudes of vibration on his finger tip and thereby tell us the relative rates of growth of loudness and vibration. Psychophysics at present is burgeoning with new and ingenious procedures for the implementation of such experiments. What follows below is by way of a progress report from midstream.

The Power Law

Perhaps the easiest way to elicit the relevant behavior from an observer is to stimulate his eye, say, with a variety of different intensities, and to ask him to assign a number proportional to the apparent magnitude of each brightness, as he sees it. Most observers, once they understand the problem, carry out this process (called magnitude estimation) with reasonable success. Not that all observers make the same estimates, or even feel any great confidence in what they are doing, but the average result for a group of normal observers turns out to be quite stable and reproducible. After all, it is the reaction of the typical (median) observer that interests us here, for we are not concerned, at the outset at least, with the fact that people differ, or that some are blind and some are photophobic. Psychophysics wants to know, first of all, what the typical input-output operating characteristics of the sensory systems are.

The typical input-output relation for all prothetic continua thus far tested is a power function. To date, the observed values of the exponent in the relation $\psi = k\phi^n$ have ranged from about 0.33 for brightness to about 3.5 for the apparent intensity of electric shock applied to the fingers. The exponent of the power function determines its curvature. If the exponent is exactly 1, the function is a straight line, and the output (reported sensation) varies linearly with the intensity of the stimulus. But when the exponent is greater than 1, the line representing the function ascends in an ever steeper slope. When it is less than 1, the curvature is the other way and the line becomes ever more horizontal.

These relations are illustrated in Figure 2, which shows examples of three perceptual continua, each having a different exponent. Electric current produces a sensation whose intensity grows more and

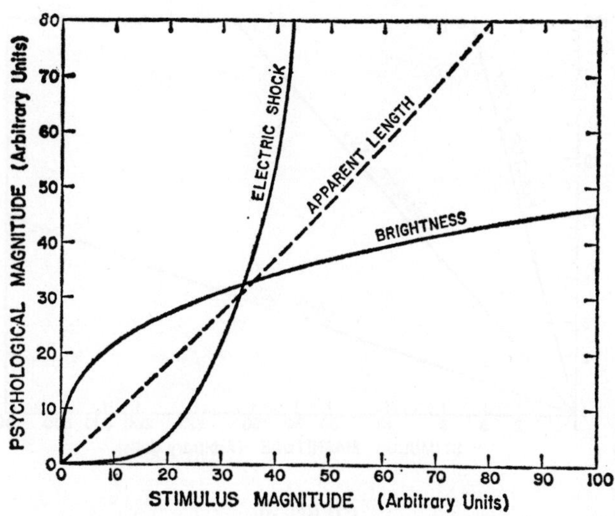

Figure 2

The apparent magnitudes of shock, length, and brightness follow different curves of growth. Their exponents are 3.5, 1.1, and 0.33, respectively. The units of the scales have been chosen arbitrarily in order to show the relative form of the curves on a single plot.

more rapidly as the current increases, whereas brightness seems to grow less and less rapidly with increasing physical intensity. As we might expect, the apparent length of a line seems to grow very nearly in direct proportion to the physical length. One foot looks about half as long as two feet—not quite, it seems, but almost.

A felicitous feature of power functions in the form they assume when graphed in log-log coordinates (logarithmic scales on both axes). The plot of a power function then becomes a straight line, and the slope of the line is a direct measure of the exponent. We can see how this works out if we make a log-log plot of the same three functions shown in Figure 2. We find that the differences in curvature in Figure 2 become differences in slope in Figure 3.

The nature of these power functions and the universality of their application testify to the existence of a profoundly simple relation between stimulus and sensory response: equal stimulus ratios pro-

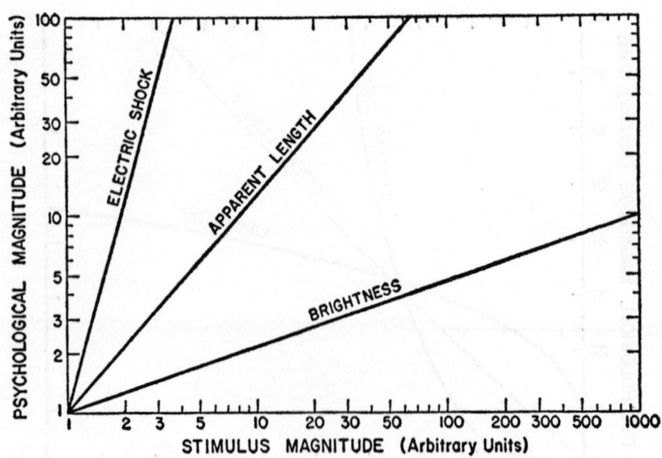

Figure 3

When the curves in Figure 2 are plotted against logarithmic coordinates, they become straight lines. The slope of the line corresponds to the exponent of the power function that governs the growth of the sensation.

duce equal subjective ratios. This is the essence of the psychophysical law. For example, it requires approximately a ninefold increase in energy to double the apparent brightness of a light, no matter where we start from in the first place. Doubling the apparent intensity of an electric shock requires an increase in current of only about 20 per cent, but this percentage increase is approximately the same all up and down the scale. On all continua governed by the power law, a constant percentage change in the stimulus produces a constant percentage change in the sensed effect.

Cross-Modality Validation

The curves in Figure 3, and many like them, were determined by asking observers to undertake, by one procedure or another, what amounted to a numerical estimation of relative sensory intensity. A scientist is properly uneasy about procedures that seem to rely on a mere expression of opinion and that seem also to depend on a fairly sophisticated acquaintance with the number system. (Naïveté about numbers is indeed an occasional source of trouble with some observers!) But the question of greatest consequence really concerns the issue of validation: Can we confirm the power law without asking observers for numerical estimations, and can we verify the predictions implicit in the type of functions plotted in Figure 3?

The nature of these predictions can most easily be expressed in terms of the lines in the log-log plots. If two sensations, loudness

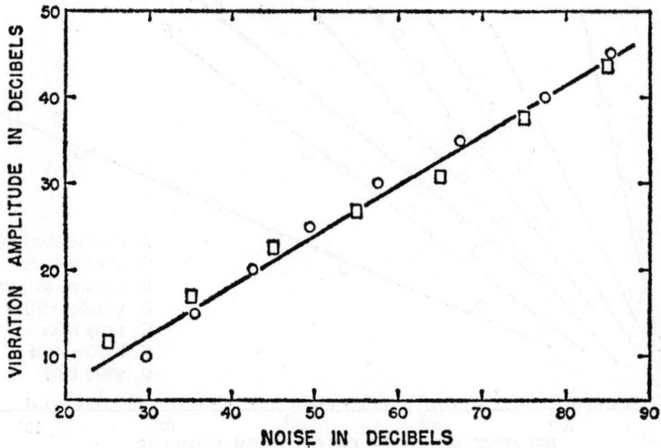

Figure 4

An equal-sensation function relating vibration (60 cycles per second) on the finger tip and the loudness of a band of noise. In one experiment the observers adjusted the loudness to match the vibration (circles); in the other they adjusted the vibration to match loudness (squares). The stimulus values are measured in terms of logarithmic scales (decibels).

and vibration, grow by different exponents (slopes), then an experiment in which the observer matches loudness to vibrations for equal apparent strength should produce a matching function that is a straight line in log-log (or decibel) coordinates. Moreover, the slope of the line should be predictable from the two original slopes, and should, in fact, be the ratio between these slopes.

A recent experiment of this kind gave a close approximation to the predicted results. Ten observers matched loudness (which had been found to grow as the 0.6 power of the sound pressure) to vibration (which grows as the 0.95 power of the amplitude), and produced a function whose slope was approximately 0.6, i.e., the ratio of 0.6 to 0.95. Figure 4 shows a plot of the data.

The success of this experiment and several similar ventures led to a bolder undertaking. If cross-modality matches can be made

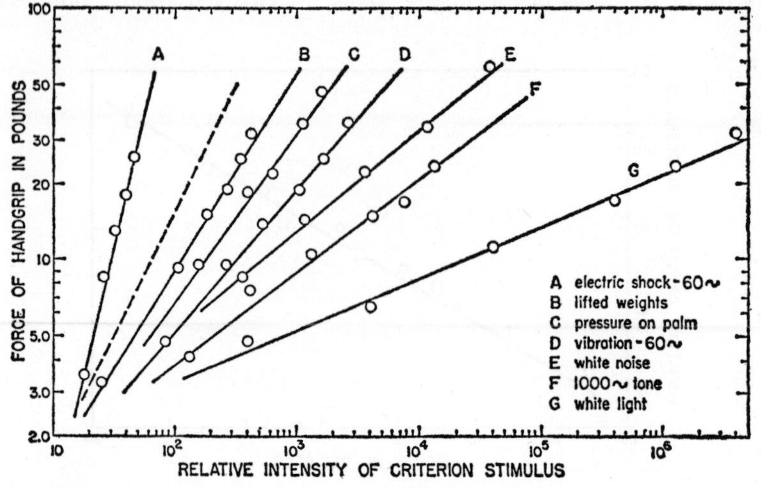

Figure 5

Growth of sensation on seven perceptual continua as measured by force of handgrip. For each value of each criterion stimulus, the observer exerted a force on a hand dynamometer in order to indicate the apparent intensity of the stimulation. Each point represents the median result for a group of ten or more observers. The relative positioning of each function along the abscissa is arbitrary. The dashed line shows a slope of 1.0 in these coordinates. Note that the lines for loudness (lines E and F) are plotted as though the abscissa represented sound pressure. If plotted against sound energy, the slopes would be similar to that for brightness (line G).

so easily, why not stimulate the observer through a sense organ and allow him to produce a matching sensory magnitude—apparent force, for example—by simply squeezing a hand dynamometer? By exerting force on a precision dynamometer, an observer can produce a sensation of strain, and at the same time activate a dial indicating the physical force exerted. In effect, then, the observer is asked to report the apparent magnitude of brightness, loudness, electric shocks, etc., by emitting appropriate squeezes instead of numerical estimates.

The actual data for seven different prothetic continua, which the observers tried to match by squeezing, are shown in Figure 5. Two features of this plot are especially interesting. All the functions approximate straight lines, precisely as the power law predicts they should, and the slopes vary from steep to flat in the manner expected. The function for electric shock rises most abruptly, proving that its exponent is large, while the function for brightness grows relatively slowly, as other evidence predicts it should.

So far so good, but a vital question remains. In order to complete the circle of validation and to exhibit all the compelling consistency that might be hoped for, we must ask whether the actual numerical values of the slopes in Figure 5 can be correctly foretold.

First, however, we must ask what happens when observers make numerical estimations of the apparent intensity or subjective force of their squeezes. In a careful and thorough experiment, my colleagues J. C. Stevens and J. D. Mack found that the apparent force of handgrip grows as the 1.7 power of the physical force applied. With this factor available, we are equipped to pose the decisive question: If the slopes in Figure 5 are multiplied by the factor 1.7, do they then equal the respective values of the slopes obtained by the method of magnitude estimation? It turns out that, within reasonably close limits, they do.

Despite the variability of human reaction, despite the relatively low precision with which a given sensory effect can be gauged, and despite the inevitable fact of individual difference, it grows increasingly clear that there is a simple and persuasive law that controls the over-all dynamics of sensory intensity. Encouraging and interesting as this may be, science of course cannot be expected to rest content without deeper understanding. Why the power law? Is this a form that is dictated, as R. D. Luce has suggested, by a kind of mathematical necessity? And what about the physiological mechanisms involved—can we look to them for further explanation of the psychophysical functions? As always happens, the discovery of a general principle susceptible of confirmation by experimental test has the effect of generating a goading sequence of new challenges. There can never be an end to this spiral in scientific work.

REFERENCES

Further details on the issues discussed in this paper may be found in:

1. W. James, *The Principles of Psychology*. New York: Holt, 1890. See Volume I, p. 546.

2. R. D. Luce, "On the Possible Psychophysical Laws," *Psycho. Rev.*, 1959, *66*: 81–95.

3. J. C. Stevens and J. D. Mack, "Scales of Apparent Force," *J. exp. Psychol.* (in press).

4. J. C. Stevens, J. D. Mack, and S. S. Stevens, "Growth of Sensation on Seven Continua as Measured by Force of Handgrip," *J. exp. Psychol.* (in press).

5. S. S. Stevens, "On the Theory of Scales of Measurement," *Science*, 1946, *103:* 677–680.

6. S. S. Stevens, "On the Psychophysical Law," *Psychol. Rev.*, 1957, *64*: 153–181.

7. S. S. Stevens, "Some Similarities between Hearing and Seeing," *Laryngoscope*, 1958, *68*: 508–527.

8. S. S. Stevens, "Measurement and Man," *Science*, 1958, *127*: 383–389.

9. S. S. Stevens, "Cross-Modality Validation of Subjective Scales for Loudness, Vibration, and Electric Shock," *J. exp. Psychol.*, 1959, *57:* 201–209.

10. S. S. Stevens, "Measurement, Psychophysics, and Utility," in C. W. Churchman and P. Ratoosh (eds.), *Measurement: Definitions and Theories.* New York, Wiley (in press).

11. S. S. Stevens, "On the Validity of the Loudness Scale," *J. acoust. Soc. Amer.*, 1959, *31:* 995–1003.

12. S. S. Stevens and E. H. Galanter, "Ratio Scales and Category Scales for a Dozen Perceptual Continua," *J. exp. Psychol.*, 1957, *54:* 377–411.

13. S. S. Stevens, A. S. Carton, and G. M. Shickman, "A Scale of Apparent Intensity of Electric Shock," *J. exp. Psychol.*, 1958, *56:* 328–334.

The Quantification of the Electrical Activity of the Nervous System*

Walter A. Rosenblith

Throughout the history of science, experimenters from different fields have dealt in a variety of ways with the problem of the quantification of their data. Technological necessities and the prevailing theoretical structure of a given field determine to a high degree the techniques of measurement that are developed and the choice of variables to be quantified. Experimenters concerned with problems of "organized complexity"[1] often made little effort to report their observations in quantitative or even systematic form. They were too aware of the limited range of experimental facts which they could ascertain with a sufficient degree of invariance and of the narrow realm in which they could actually verify predictions from mathematical models.

These difficulties, and an overly narrow interpretation of the doctrine so eloquently stated by Lord Kelvin,† have contributed to the fact that many neurophysiologists, for example, have hesitated to go beyond reporting raw data in a somewhat phenomenological

* An earlier, shorter version of this chapter constitutes Chapter 1 of the Technology Press Research Monograph entitled "Processing Neuroelectric Data," by the Communications Biophysics Group of Research Laboratory of Electronics and William M. Siebert (1959).

† "I often say that when you can measure what you are speaking about, and express it in numbers, you know something about it; but when you cannot express it in numbers, your knowledge is of a meagre and unsatisfactory kind; it may be the beginning of knowledge, but you have scarcely, in your thoughts, advanced to the stage of Science, whatever the matter may be." Contrast this view of Lord Kelvin's with Gödel's contention[2] that "it is purely an historical accident that it [mathematics] developed along quantitative lines."

manner. Such an attitude renders communication with fellow scientists hazardous. If verbal statements alone are made to carry the informational burden of large bodies of data, friendly model-makers—most of whom come from the ranks of the physical sciences—are tempted to construct theories of "how the brain works" on the basis of a few isolated and easily mathematized facts.

But it was not just caprice or lack of farsightedness among the data-rich and theory-poor scientists that produced this mismatch between their vast labors and the relatively small amount of theoretically integrated knowledge that became available. They were handicapped by a lack of adequate data-processing facilities and by the fact that the mathematical models of classical physics (and certainly those of quantum physics) had little to offer to the student of the nervous system or of human behavior. Hence many of them became interested in cybernetics,[3] which emerged as the philosophical expression of the communications technology of the postwar period. It was under cybernetic auspices that numerous problems relating to the behavior of complex living systems were reconsidered. Only too often did these reconsiderations turn out to be suggestive but also frustrating. At that stage a search for general principles of the behavior of the nervous system could hardly help being somewhat superficial. The neuroanatomical, neuro-physiological, and behavioral data extant were not in a form that made theorizing at an over-all level meaningful.

Measurement and Analysis in Electrophysiology

For more than two centuries—thanks to various species of electric fish—men have been aware of the existence of "animal electricity." More than a century ago Helmholtz measured the conduction velocity of nerve, and throughout the second half of the nineteenth century an appreciable amount of knowledge concerning brain potential was accumulated. In a recent review of the rise of neurophysiology in the nineteenth century, Brazier[4] summarized the situation at the end of that century as follows: "It was known that the brain had 'spontaneous' electric activity, that potential shifts could be elicited in the appropriate cortical areas by sensory stimulation, that these potentials could be recorded from the skull and that anesthesia abolished them." However, electrophysiology entered its period of rapid growth only after the technology of the vacuum tube had given us amplifiers and oscilloscopes. These two instruments permitted electrophysiologists to increase the sensitivity of their observations and to display even rapidly fluctuating bioelectric potentials as a function of time.

The characteristic deflections or patterns in voltage-versus-time displays constitute the electrophysiologist's basic data. But what is an adequate description of a complex waveform? As long as we deal with DC potentials or sinusoids, an instrument that yields one or two characteristic numbers is perfectly satisfactory; but when we attempt to assess arbitrary wave forms containing sharp "transients" and "noise," several questions arise. Is the voltmeter (even the vacuum-tube voltmeter) the appropriate instrument of measurement? Is it necessary to display the complete waveform by photographing it from the face of an oscilloscope? Can we find selective transformations upon the data that yield meaningful descriptions while reducing the total amount of information displayed?

A discussion of appropriate methods for the quantification of electrophysiological data leads us to consider two issues that the physical sciences have faced—sometimes quite explicitly and sometimes less so—throughout their history. Before we make measurements reflecting the behavior of complex systems, it may be wise to ask ourselves two sets of questions. Why do we make a particular measurement? What conclusions (regarding the phenomena under investigation) shall we be able to draw on the basis of the measurement?

The first set of questions inquires into the purposes of the experimenting electrophysiologist: Is he interested in relating the electrical events that he records from an isolated nerve fiber to the physicochemical processes that occur in the transmission of a nerve impulse? Is he using the electrical events in order to trace certain pathways in the nervous system? Is he trying to study the responses of certain neural structures to carefully controlled sensory stimuli? Is he investigating the behavior of these structures in relation to a mathematical model that he has formulated? Is he studying the way in which certain chemical substances affect synaptic transmission? Is he trying to relate changes in an organism's electrical activity to conditioning or learning? Or is he concerned with the presence or absence of certain patterns in this activity with a view toward clinical diagnosis? Neurophysiology includes all of these experiments.

The experimenter's purpose determines the choice of his variables and the display technique for his data, and it affects the very definition of what constitutes an experiment—that is, which parameters are to be held constant, and how replicable phenomena must be. Neurophysiology—which has, compared to the physical sciences, little theoretical structure of its own—is thus characterized by an aggregate of techniques for the study of the nervous system and of its component parts. As a science, it stands in close relation to such fields as neuroanatomy, sensory physiology, biochemistry, biophysics, psychology, and medicine, and the significance of neurophysiological findings is often assessed in terms of their relevance to these neighboring fields.

The second set of questions concerns the inferences that can be drawn from electrophysiological "pointer readings." It is here that our lack of understanding of the organizational principles and of the mechanisms of the nervous system is felt most seriously. The overall organizational structure of this nonhomogeneous medium that consists of large numbers of highly specific elements has, so far, defied useful descriptions. Much effort has gone into analyzing the fine structure of its various components in terms of current biophysical and biochemical knowledge, but up to now these efforts have not yielded an approach capable of dealing with the unique properties that characterize the nervous system of higher animals. Here is a system that is composed of many interacting units (all of which are by no means alike), that is organized both flexibly and hierarchically, and that consists of subsystems (enjoying various degrees of autonomy) capable of fulfilling specific and/or nonspecific functions. Here is a system that reacts more reliably and predictably to informationally rich quasi-natural stimuli than to contrived but mathematically "simple" ones. Here is a system that is capable of learning and of giving reasonably reliable performance throughout an extended period of time, with all the safety factors and maintenance and repair requirements that such performance demands.

What is the type of electrical activity whose study will yield the "systems neurophysiology" that underlies the behavior of information-processing organisms? What strategy should we adopt in dealing with the signals that we record from the nervous system—signals whose code is known so incompletely? Should we attempt to isolate a single neuron and study its behavior in great detail, hoping that we will pick a typical one capable of representing a not very well-defined population?* Should we, at the other extreme, work only with the muffled polyneural roar that is able to make itself "heard" through man's thick skull? Should we limit ourselves to studying recordings of the "spontaneous" activity of a neuron (or of neuronal populations)—that is, the activity that we can still observe after we have turned off all the stimulus generators that are under our control? Or should we study stimulus-response relations—that is, those response events whose occurrence is linked by some criterion, usually a temporal one, to the delivery of a definable stimulus? Can we assume that these latter stimulus-evoked events will always simply add to the "spontaneous background activity," or must we examine their interdependence in different physiological states of the organism?

Are the biggest voltages, especially when recorded at the outside of the skull, the most important ones to study? If we compare this situation with the facts of speech communication, we find that it is the vowels (indeed, their first formants) that carry most of the energy among the speech sounds, although—in English at least—it is the consonants that carry most of the linguistic information. There are perhaps other lessons to be drawn from the study of speech communication. When a Fourier analysis of speech signals is carried out, the vowels (whose duration is of the order of 1/10 second) seem to be represented much more meaningfully by Fourier

* We are, of course, far from knowing how to synthesize explicitly integrated behavior of the nervous system from existing data on the behavior of components. We are also severely limited when we want to design experiments according to the separation-of-variables paradigm. This problem of what Warren Weaver has recently called the "dissectability" of a complex organized system shimmers through a good many of the more philosophical arguments in biology. "Dissectability" rears its head in the various versions of the vitalism controversy; it is inherent in the contrast between *in vivo* and *in vitro* experiments; it contaminates the choice of how "low" an animal we dare pick in our quest to understand the discrimination of visual forms or even of human speech.

components than the consonants. The latter can be viewed as "transients" or "transitionals," whose spectral composition depends much more upon the vowels that precede or follow them. The problem of where the vowels end and the consonants start (technically known as the *segmentation* problem) presents a challenge all of its own, comparable perhaps to that of defining the *duration* of an evoked response. An "ah" will exhibit rather different spectral components when pronounced by a man, a woman, or a child; it will even exhibit appreciable differences when pronounced repeatedly, and in different context, by the same individual. And yet there is something invariant about it that makes it recognizable as an "ah." This "ah"-ness is not anything that is easily characterizable by absolute numbers, but rather by distinctive features[5] or parametrically defined patterns, by certain relations among the components of a sound, especially in relation to other sounds that might have been emitted. Lest this analogy be carried too far, let us not behave as if we expected somebody to break "the" code of the nervous system. We are aiming to discover the relevant units of analysis, those distinctive features of neural signals that will help us organize the innumerable data that we can record from the nervous system.

What are the techniques of analysis that are readily available to electrophysiologists for dealing with the range of experimental problems mentioned above? Let us briefly mention some sample techniques that have been used. The mathematics of circuit analysis, at least in its simpler forms, assumes that the circuits and their components are linear, lumped, finite, passive, and bilateral.[6] It would, of course, be absurd to pretend that the nervous system or its components have these properties, though it may be possible to find, by applying circuit theory, in what manner the behavior of a sensory system, for example, deviates from this model.

If we restrict ourselves to dealing with whatever wave forms may have been recorded, we must ask whether specific techniques, such as Fourier analysis or correlation analysis, are actually appropriate to the particular experimental question. Such techniques imply that the time series to be analyzed satisfy certain conditions. Obviously, the assumptions implicit in these analytical techniques are a price that we have to pay for their use. Physical scientists also pay this price. They, however, know a great deal more about the processes underlying the phenomena they study than we know about the mechanisms underlying neuroelectric phenomena. Thus, in physical science there is a better chance of adjusting and correcting models than there is in neurophysiology. And yet the student of the nervous system has little choice until more appropriate techniques of analysis have been developed. He must utilize those that are available in order to find out where they cease to fit. He may, nevertheless, want to take the precaution of assembling a sufficient body of apparently consistent data before getting involved in ambitious computations.

Is there a moral that imposes itself in the light of the preceding tedious and yet incomplete enumeration of problems that one faces in this type of research? We believe that there is, and we believe that it can be stated in a single word: pluralism. At this stage of our knowledge of the nervous system, only a pluralistic strategy guarantees that we will not blind ourselves to useful approaches because we have prematurely committed ourselves to one of them. The very multiplicity of purposes precludes rigid prescriptions of experimental design or methods of data processing and analysis on intrinsic grounds. We must, rather, be prepared to make our choice on the basis of extrinsic values or influence. Our background, our biases of interest, our physical and intellectual surroundings, and the *Zeitgeist* have led us to opt for certain methods of data processing and certain types of mathematical models. We believe that these techniques are capable of coming to grips with the statistical character of neural activity, which is one of the essential features of the nervous system. We have, furthermore, a preference for packaging our results in a form that is reasonably quantitative; that is, we try to express as many of our findings as we can in *some* mathematical representation without always trying to fit our data to analytical functions. Since we are dealing with a multivariate system, we are not surprised that the patterns and relationships we find are often statistical. Finally, it is fair to say that although we feel more secure when we have the guiding influence of a mathematical model and of a relevant physiological mechanism in our experiments, we are not so narrow-minded as to ignore the usefulness and even the beauty of a good classification scheme that orders variables whose importance to the organism is undeniable.

A Statistical View of Neuroelectric Events

When we assess the sensory performance of higher organisms,[7] certain characteristics emerge that suggest problems for a quantitative study of the electrical activity of the nervous system. As we consider organisms engaged in communication tasks, it becomes apparent (*a*) that their performance is statistical in character; (*b*) that they need more time to handle more "information"; (*c*) that their capacity to discriminate and their speed of reaction depend on stimulus intensity; and (*d*) that their repertory of absolute identifications (Miller's "span of absolute judgement"[8]) is relatively small and seemingly based upon the ability to make several rather crude discriminations simultaneously—that is, to classify environmental sensory inflow into some rather gross categories.

We are thus led in our studies to emphasize statistical and temporal aspects of the electrical behavior of the nervous system and to look for over-all—relatively gross and stable—patterns in this behavior. This quasi-thermodynamic approach is not intended to deprecate the complementary view that derives from statistical mechanics, but it again points toward the hiatus that exists between what a microelectrode (particularly an intracellular one) sees, and the multifarious role played, for example, by an entire relay nucleus in a sensory system. In so-called ablation experiments such a structure is often removed in order to elucidate its role; however, the logical interpretation of the resulting deficits in performance is far from unambiguous. The interpretation hinges on one's model of the nervous system: Is it a collection of simple reflex arcs, or is it populated by complex feedback loops; is function strictly localized, or are there many functionally equipotential spare parts?

No matter which aspect of the electrical activity of the nervous system we study, we always face the task of defining "typical events" among those we observe experimentally. This task confronts the experimenter whether his concern is with responses evoked by sensory stimuli or with the electroencephalogram (EEG): he has to establish certain criteria of judgment. His criteria will be different when he records population responses with the aid of macroelectrodes and when he studies the activity of a single cell with the aid of a microelectrode. Furthermore, the electrophysiologist must decide when two observations are "identical." The identity-defining operation may range from identity in one aspect of the event only (such as occurrence or nonoccurrence of a so-called all-or-none spike) to identity in several measurable aspects, such as average spike latency,* distribution of spike latencies, and so on.

In order to decide whether an event is typical and whether two events differ, we should have an expectation of the distribution of possible events. This distribution might be estimated from observations of evoked responses to a large number of identical stimuli, or from repeated samplings of EEG traces. Actually, experimenters rarely have such information available to them; if they are well trained, they choose representative records as illustrations for their papers. It is, nevertheless, necessary to realize that few, if any, systematic studies have been made to assess an experimenter's information handling capacity as applied to his ability to view oscilloscopic traces or examine film records. In other words, we do not really know how safe current procedures are.

We have tried to present and review elsewhere ([9, 10, 11]) some of the available evidence on the statistical character of input-output relations for single neurons or for responses from populations of neuronal elements. Here we shall try to summarize the essential arguments only. We first faced this problem when we tried to find criteria for deciding what constituted a typical evoked response—that is, an electrophysiological event that is triggered by the presentation of a discrete stimulus, most often a sensory one. There exists, to our knowledge, no generally accepted operational definition of what is meant by an evoked response, although the concept has been exceedingly useful in electrophysiological and neuroanatomical studies of the nervous system.

Let us briefly see how evoked responses are recorded. The experimenter usually controls the instant of delivery of the stimulus. Ordinarily, he then establishes the presence or absence of an evoked response by either of two methods or by the two methods conjointly: (*a*) In recording with macroelectrodes, he detects visually the presence of a characteristic wave form or deflection. (*b*) In recording with microelectrodes, he detects aurally (and/or visually) a change in the acoustic signals that represent the electrical

* The *latency* of a response measures the delay from the instant at which the stimulus was presented.

events "seen" by the microelectrode after these events have been appropriately amplified and transduced into sound.

As should be clear from this description, the experimenter's ability to detect such changes in visual and/or aural displays depends upon how stable these changes are in relation to the patterns of "background activity."* The ease with which such changes are detected depends upon how soon they occur following stimulus presentation and how much they exceed the experimenter's just-noticeable difference for the particular sensory pattern involved.

For responses recorded with macroelectrodes, there is variability with respect to both amplitude and time. The evoked responses of the classical sensory pathways exhibit relatively short latencies and little variability in latency. It is this relative stability of the temporal aspects of these responses that makes the use of averaging by computing devices possible and useful. Thus far, no convenient techniques have been developed that yield summary descriptions of electrical events that have longer and more variable latencies; the so-called blocking of the alpha rhythm is an example of such events, whose latencies are comparable to the latencies of behavioral acts.

For responses recorded from single units with the aid of microelectrodes, the variability problem poses itself in a rather different manner. Here we are dealing with a set of discrete events which are quite comparable in wave shape and amplitude, but which occur at latencies that are governed by both stimulus parameters and the prevailing sequences of "spontaneous" firings of the cell. The changes in the patterns of spontaneous firing that do occur may result in either increases ("excitation") or decreases ("inhibition") in average firing frequency. Thus, variability may now affect (*a*) changes in the number of firings per unit time (how many spikes does a given stimulus elicit or inhibit?); (*b*) "first"-spike latency (latency of the spike whose occurrence is most directly linked to the delivery of the stimulus); (*c*) interspike intervals, and so on.

* We mentioned above the problems of the typicality of a response and of the identity of two responses. These problems include in some sense decisions of how typical the background activity is in which these responses are imbedded. Amassian and his co-workers have emphasized only recently[12] how much the presence of spontaneous cell discharges complicates the analysis of the effect of stimulus variables.

The problem of adequate detection and description of evoked responses led us to experimental procedures in which computers were instructed to "look" for changes in patterns of ongoing activity that are somehow linked to the delivery of stimuli. "Looking" for changes in averages, such as means, or for changes in the distribution of events within several time intervals becomes thus a method of search in which the properly programmed computer supplements human capacities. We also had to find ways of dealing with the undeniable fact that repeated presentations of the same stimulus are far from yielding "identical" neuroelectric responses in truly physiological preparations. Instead of abdicating before this fact by declaring that neuroelectric activity is not truly quantifiable, we propose to take advantage of this difficulty. The variabilities that are observed seem to have their own regularities, which are, in turn, related to both stimulus and organismic variables. By constructing probabilistic models that gave economical descriptions of responses from populations of neurons, several workers[13] were able to test how thoroughly we understood certain neural events in the auditory system. In addition, their models led to experimentation that was novel and productive of further insights.

If we look for an interpretation of satistical neuronal behavior, we must first of all consider the complexity of the system or subsystem under study, the multiplicity of possible interactions,* and the inadequacy of our description of the "state" in which a neuron, a population of neurons, or even more generally the nervous system finds itself at the time of stimulus presentation.

In a recent article Bullock[15] presents a thoughtful discussion of the present status of the neuron doctrine and then suggests several major revisions. The neurophysiological evidence from intracellular recordings forces a reconsideration of what we mean by "the" state of a neuron and emphasizes the necessity for looking beyond the occurrence or nonoccurrence of the spike potential as the sole indicator of neuronal function. This awareness of the importance of potential changes other than spike discharges did not come about

* Sholl (14), who has discussed the quantification of neuronal connectivity, comes to the conclusion that "impulses arriving along a single primary visual fiber will be dispersed among the 5,000 neurons distributed around its terminal branches."

suddenly. It was Bishop[16] who, after a critical review of the characteristics of *graded* and *all-or-none* responses, concluded "that the graded response type is more general, as well as more primitive, than the all-or-none response and that the latter developed when an early metazoan became too large, or underwent separation of functionally related parts to too great a distance, for graded responses to be effective as a means of communication between them." Bishop's account of neural processes and mechanisms leads him to state that "the chief physiological business of the nervous system is transacted in graded response elements" and that "what we do, mentally or physically, is probably to express the state of excitability of the graded response tissue that initiates impulses in axonal conductors." These remarks are highly relevant to the way in which we can expect to quantify the activity of the nervous system. There is little basis for hoping to find *one* ideal measure that will permit quantification at all levels of neural organization and for all sizes of neural aggregates. And although more adequate descriptions of the behavior of single neurons or of neuronal populations will undoubtedly become available, there remains serious doubt whether we shall, in the foreseeable future, be able to dispense with statistical descriptions of neuroelectric phenomena.

Categorization and Quantification

Up to this point we have not dealt explicitly with the view—or should we say the prejudice—according to which the maturity of a science is a function of the number of quantitative concepts it uses. This position reflects the image of a world perceived in terms of nineteenth-century physics.

The contemporary philosopher of science Feigl[17] expresses the opinions of many a scientist when he distinguishes a hierarchy of logical concepts that proceeds from (*a*) purely qualitative or classificatory concepts via (*b*) semi-quantitative or rank-ordering concepts to (*c*) fully quantitative or metrical ones. Feigl adds that "once it becomes possible to introduce an operational definition of equality of intervals and some (often quite conventional) fixation of a zero point and of a unit of scale, we deal with metrical concepts pertaining to measurable magnitudes or *scientific* [italics ours] variables."

When a scientist is concerned—one might almost say involved—with several levels of scientific inquiry,* the problem of reductionism poses itself forcefully. A reductionist approach attempts to derive the properties of a more highly organized system from either structural or functional properties of the pre-existing elements at the "lower" level. What are the rules according to which one set of concepts gets transformed into a set that is operative at a different level? Is there a scientific currency that is freely convertible from the study of cosmic rays to the study of sensory perception, from the highly controlled laboratory environment of nuclear accelerators to the almost indifferent environment in which human beings, designed by evolution, communicate by speech? Does energy, or perhaps information (in the form of generalized entropy), constitute the reductionist thread that will permit us to demonstrate that biology—which encompasses the behavior of the whole animal—is "nothing but physics" (which now subsumes chemistry)? What a challenging program! Rare indeed is the working biological scientist whose implicit faith is not that of an ultimate reductionist; he does not expect the biophysics of the nervous system to contradict the laws of physics (of physical physics, that is). And yet just as solid-state physics has to worry about more than the behavior of the hydrogen atom, biophysics and its allied disciplines need freedom to explore their own levels of complexity; that is, those relations between physical elements which make for specificity and adaptation, for reproduction and learning.

Every reductionist scheme runs, sooner or later, into the perplexing problem of recoding continuity into discreteness and discreteness into continuity. The nervous system faces this problem repeatedly and successfully, but thus far it has not let us even peek at its general solution to this problem. What follows suggests nothing more than a direction in which speculation regarding certain relevant issues might proceed.

A highly evolved organism faces tasks that transcend reductionist

*He might, for instance, try to predict the sensory performance of organisms on the basis of the neuroanatomy of the sensory pathways or from the findings of sensory electrophysiology.

models that would restrict the mechanisms involved in the handling of sensory information to "high-fidelity" transformations of the stimulus. A sensory message is more than a sequence of eidola. The organism must be free to attend selectively to signals in the midst of distractions; it must be able to extract the biologically relevant information-bearing elements from redundant signals. Such behaviors center about a "gimmick" known to a variety of communicators (dramatists, cartoonists, teachers, propagandists): *distortion for the sake of emphasis.* The organism therefore subjects the incoming stimuli to a variety of "abstracting" transformations at all levels* of the nervous system. The products of these more or less stimulus-faithful transformations are then available for further processing by both the specific and the less specific[18] parts of the nervous system. Instead of being faced *ab initio* with the necessity of deciding where the stimulus belongs along an infinitely divisible continuum, the organism starts by detecting the presence or absence of certain (not even necessarily orthogonal) features of the stimulus. Once this multidimensional nominal scaling[19] has been accomplished, the organism may either refine the measurement operations or may continue in the previous vein if the categorial[20] response mode suffices. We know that multidimensional categorial responses are extremely noise-resistant when man deals with speech sounds or with visual forms. Much biologically important communication can be analyzed in terms of similar concepts. This is hardly the place, however, to speculate whether these distinctive features are learned, innate, or imprintable in a given species.

In addition, man and his closest relatives in the animal kingdom possess the capability of going beyond the categorial mode: They can supplement and refine it by a variety of *vernier* modes along a given dimension.[19] The transition from multidimensional qualitative judgments to more and more quantitative ones is apparently fairly smooth. It thus becomes both idle and artificial to cut this continuum of performance in the informational domain by telling us that now man quantifies, and now he only categorizes.

* The traditional opposition between so-called peripheral and central mechanisms (or between "lower" and higher" levels in the nervous system) has lost much of its significance in the light of recent evidence on the centrifugal control of sensory inflow.[18]

NOTES

1. W. Weaver, "Science and Complexity," *Amer. Scientist,* 1948, *36,* 536–544.

2. J. R. Oppenheimer, "Analogy in Science," *Amer. Psychologist,* 1956, *11:* 127–135.

3. N. Wiener, *Cybernetics,* New York; Wiley, 1948.

4. M. A. B. Brazier, "Rise of Neurophysiology in the 19th Century," *J. Neurophysiol.,* 1957, *20:* 212–226.

5. R. Jakobson and M. Halle, *Fundamentals of Language,* Gravenhage: Mouton, 1956.

6. E. A. Guillemin, *Introductory Circuit Theory,* New York: Wiley, 1953.

7. W. A. Rosenblith, "Sensory Performance of Organisms," *Revs. mod. Phys.,* 1959, *31:* 485–491.

8. G. A. Miller, "The Magical Number Seven, Plus or Minus Two: Some Limits on Our Capacity for Processing Information," *Psychol. Rev.,* 1956, *63:* 81–97.

9. W. A. Rosenblith, "Some Electrical Responses from the Auditory Nervous System," *Proceedings of the Symposium on Information Networks* (Polytechnical Institute of Brooklyn, April 12–14, 1954), pp. 223–247.

10. L. S. Frishkopf and W. A. Rosenblith, "Fluctuations in Neural Thresholds," in H. P. Yockey, R. L. Platzman, and H. Quastler (eds.), *Symposium on Information Theory in Biology,* New York: Pergamon Press, 1958, 153–168.

11. W. A. Rosenblith, "Some Quantifiable Aspects of the Electrical Activity of the Nervous System (with Emphasis upon Responses to Sensory Stimuli)," *Revs. mod. Phys.,* 1959, *31:* 532–545.

12. V. E. Amassian, L. Berlin, J. Macy, Jr., and H. J. Waller, "II. Simultaneous Recordings of the Activities of Several Individual Cortical Neurons," *Trans. New York Acad. Sci.,* 1959, *21:* 395–405.

13. M. H. Goldstein, Jr., "A Statistical Model for Interpreting Neuroelectric Responses," *Information and Control,* 1960, *3:* 1–17.

14. D. A. Sholl, *The Organization of the Cerebral Cortex,* New York: Wiley, 1956.

15. T. H. Bullock, "Neuron Doctrine and Electrophysiology," *Science,* 1959, *129:* 997–1002.

16. G. H. Bishop, "Natural History of the Nerve Impulse," *Physiol. Revs.,* 1956, *36:* 376–399.

17. H. Feigl, "Levels of Scientific Inquiry," *Univ. Minn. med. Bull.,* 1956, *28:* 90–97.

18. H. W. Magoun, *The Waking Brain,* Springfield, Ill.: Charles C Thomas, 1958.

19. See the paper and references by S. S. Stevens in this volume.

20. J. S. Bruner, "Neural Mechanisms in Perception," *Psychol. Rev.,* 1957, *64:* 340–358.

The Qualitative and the Quantitative in Political and Legal Analysis

Harold D. Lasswell

The problems that cluster about quality-quantity relationships in political and legal analysis have to do with (1) the formulation of theory, (2) the procedures of data-gathering and processing, and (3) the interpretation of the significance of the scientific enterprise in the social context of which it is a part and with which it interacts.

The Formulation of Theory

Whatever impression may have been created by Marxist polemics at any given time, it is obvious that socialist theory has assumed that both qualitative and quantitative categories are indispensable components of scientific thought. The same assumption appears in every branch of political and legal inquiry, if one is willing to say that this distinction relates to the interplay between *context* and the *specification of context*. Even a casual inspection of the literature confirms the point that, when discussions are about the frame of reference within which inquiry proceeds, terms such as "qualitative" enter into the debate; when the stress is upon a rather precise connection of theoretical models with a field of observation, the recurring term is some variant of "quantity." With certain exceptions to be noted presently, it is recognized that these are complementary parts of the whole intellectual task. Specification is essential if theory is to be put into operation; contextual constructs are essential if new lines of investigation are to be opened up. Actually, the interplay between these intellectual tasks is more subtle and interpenetrative than this mode of phrasing the matter may suggest. The challenge to translate general conceptions into operational indexes, for example, typically brings into focus the usefulness of introducing a series of intermediate categories of diminishing generality. Conversely, the results obtained by describing a situation in highly specific terms call attention to the idiosyncrasies of the local context when viewed in a wider setting, and lead to some revision of the categories of general reference.

Let us consider the two categories by which social processes (and hence legal and political processes) have often been characterized, namely, "material" and "ideological." The "material" category, at the time it was introduced, was richer in specific, measurable connotations than the "ideological." Hence the expected returns from scientific effort appeared to be greater by studying the material itself than by studying ideological factors. Any attempt to specify the "material" calls for the introduction of subcategories. "Bushels per acre" is acceptable as an index of some forms of production (a material factor). But what measures the production of an entertainer or a propagandist? Is all production to be labeled "material," or are nonmaterial outcomes (such as laughter or belief) to be rejected as "production"? If the "material" is defined as including the technology of production, does the word "technology" cover the habits of the skilled worker, the knowledge of the engineer, the administrative strategies in factory organization, and the legal regulation of contractual agreements? Or are these phenomena more conveniently called "ideological"?

For many years the lines between "material" and "ideological" categories remained vague, partly because convenient indexes of the latter were missing. The scholars of our civilization think easily in specifics that refer to "thing" events, like bushels and bricks. They are less ready to translate into specifics when dealing with events that are variously called ideology, belief, legal norm, loyalty, knowledge, and the like. As a beginning student of politics, I recall my dissatisfaction on realizing that, while economists were plentifully equipped with data about goods and prices, for instance, political scientists were poorly supplied with comparable data showing trends and correlations in political or legal events. Many scholars from many fields and many schools, including Marxists, were singularly vague about the precise interplay between "ideological" and "material" factors. I searched for ways of specifying these elusive ideological elements.

It was not too difficult, of course, to characterize the simpler aspects of a decision. For a long time voting statistics showing the results of popular elections have been kept; these could be used to specify the rise or fall of parties and individuals. Legislatures, executive and administrative agencies, and courts have kept records (with various degrees of completeness) of their own votes; these could be analyzed. But such operations did not carry us far. What factors directly affected voters, legislators, judges? In short, what events, presented at the focus of attention of the decision-maker and acting upon his predispositions (within the constraints of the current situation), accounted for the final outcome? How were these to be described in specific terms? How, in short, were such conceptions as constitutional consensus, underlying philosophy, spirit of the time, class ethos, and the like to be translated operationally?

Such questions led me to emphasize a greatly neglected category in political, legal, and indeed all social analysis, to wit, the focus of attention. To deal systematically with the focus of attention, we developed and applied methods of counting units of reference in the content of communication. Techniques of the kind (quantitative semantics) make it possible to use similar terms to compare what lawyers and witnesses say to the court, or what the courts say in justifying decisions (opinions). It is practicable to study not only what comes to the attention of the judge and jury in the courtroom, but what they say or write to one another during formal deliberations and informal contacts. The judge may be affected by what comes over television and radio during his leisure hours, as well as by what appears in newspapers, magazines, and law journals, or what is brought to his notice at home, at the club, and elsewhere. A comparable analysis applies to each voter (and voting group), legislator (and legislature), and any other participant in the politico-legal or the social process at large.

The techniques of content analysis, therefore, were an outcome of the pursuit of specificity within a comprehensive frame of social analysis; in turn, they accentuated the role of a category of events important in all interactions. For instance, in many instances "material" changes affect one another indirectly by first affecting patterns of attention, thereby inducing modifications of demand, expectation, and identification, which in turn influence behavioral expressions. Thus a flood that washes away bridges and retaining walls may do all its damage on only one side of a river as a result of someone's decision to concentrate protective efforts on the most valuable physical property, which lies on the other bank. "Ideological" innovations (such as a scientific hypothesis) typically affect other ideological factors by initiating intermediate sequences of events which combine "material" and "ideological." In short, all factors referred to by such categories are interactive throughout the entire socio-historical process.

The Number and Character of Key Categories

I have been describing some intellectual operations that either "fill in" or "expand" the original frame of reference. Another possible rearrangement is a change in the number of categories used at comparable levels of generality. I have been referring to a theory with a two-term set of high-level categories, "material" and "ideological." My impression is that as empirical research has proceeded in the social sciences, these categories have been losing their former hold. Today the "material" is less plausibly set off from the "ideological" than it was. It is more in keeping with present perspectives to refer to "events" (subjective or not), and to assume that the operational indexes of "subjective events" will include both words and nonwords. In modern medicine, for example, we take it for granted that some patients can be more expeditiously handled by communication ("psychic") therapy than by noncommunication ("somatic") methods. Or a combination of methods can be employed; for example, "brain washing" involves both communication and noncommunication procedures.

In fact, two-term category sets are yielding to multiterm sets (in the interest of social process analysis). We are recognizing the convenience of emphasizing several value outcomes in the social process. Students of economics focus upon transaction outcomes involving wealth (claims to goods and services). Students of politics and law concentrate upon decisions involving power. My colleagues and

I use six other categories to designate the other value outcomes in the social process (respect, enlightenment, affection, well-being, rectitude, skill). The process as a whole is characterized as man seeking to maximize value outcomes, within the constraints imposed by his total situation. All value-shaping and sharing activities are patterned—each pattern being a "practice" composed of "perspectives" and "operations"—and include in varying degree the use of the natural resource environment. The important methodological point is not this set of specific categories, but the employment at a systematic multivalue contextual model of all social process events.

Within a contextual framework there is need of many systematic models of partial processes, such as the economic or political. This contrasts with the past tendency, especially among non-Marxist thinkers, to devise partial models irrespective of their relation to the context. Some such partial models have led to highly successful results, notably in economic analyses of some aggregate market activities. But there are disadvantages connected with the emphasizing of highly formal systematic models connected only inadvertently with the social setting of which they are part. The result may be sterile scholasticism (as in the case of some academic economics); and there may be disillusioned revolts against systematic theory itself (as in many schools of business or public administration).

Systematic Contextual Systems

The central point as related to the present discussion is this: If the details of any social process are to be properly compared with the details of any other, and if a comprehensive social science is to be developed, detailed patterns must be located in terms of the same comprehensive map of the whole social context.

It is generally recognized among social historians with a world view that Marxist analysis has had, and continues to have, a strong appeal to the intellectually alert on strictly intellectual grounds, quite apart from other motivations, such as power or respect. As we have implied before, a factor that has contributed to the spread of Marxist analysis is the weight given to "material" factors and to the bodies of "quantitative" information available in support of theses alleging the decisive role of the material component. Socialist scholarship has never hesitated to take quantitative information in stride. But the impact of Marxism among scientists and scholars in many countries is also—perhaps chiefly—connected with the success of its systematic contextual categories in providing a frame of reference for the organizing of knowledge. When one interviews students and more mature intellectuals in any country or looks into intimate life-history records, a conspicuous fact is the sense of orientation that Marxist theory has given to so many of them. A common metaphor refers to Marxism as the turning on of a switch that suddenly suffuses a room with light, enabling one to see that the object against which he bumped his knee was a chair, and the cloth he had touched was a tapestry. Hitherto miscellaneous specifics fall into context. We all use this type of metaphor to convey the idea that some exceptional enlightenment has come to us.

Many intellectuals respond in the same way to Spengler or Toynbee, or, on a more restricted scale, to Max Weber, Schumpeter, or Karl Polanyi. These writers are often believed to do for the narrower field of human history and social process what religious teachers and metaphysicians have done for a less empirical realm. All these thinkers, however sound or unsound, have been systematically and comprehensively contextual. Those who deal with history and society provide a frame of reference (inclusive in space, time, and figure) regarding the event-manifold of yesterday, today, and tomorrow.

Suppose we strip the Marxist formulations of self-serving declarations about their "absolute truth" or the "inevitability" of what is said about future events, events that lie beyond contemporary observation. In a formal sense, declarations of the kind are not pertinent if we limit ourselves to what is designative and is actually or potentially open to observation. If we look at these writers in this more technical and restricted framework, it may be possible to uncover something of general importance to our principal interest—the structure of contextual systems.

The "Loose" Connection between Theory and Data

A preliminary point concerns the relatively "loose" connection between many categories of such systems and the data on hand at any given cross section in time. In part, the relative looseness comes from the lack of carefully defined indexes systematically applied to available evidence, such as would make accessible to the investigator comparable data regarding trends and distributions, and would foster the discovery of correlations among various factor combinations. Even where operational indexes exist, there are regrettable gaps. Did you ever try to ascertain the voting record of courts, executive and administrative tribunals, legislatures, and electorates in this country as of the past year? Or ten years ago? Or a century back? Or have you had occasion to examine the present state of basic trend, distribution, and correlation information about the relative frequency with which the courts have invoked particular constitutional clauses, past decisions and opinions, in cases in which comparable parties were making comparable claims, represented by comparable counsel, growing out of comparable precipitating events? If so, you are well briefed about the spottiness of the reports now at hand, and recognize why we have put so much stress upon the importance of designing a more satisfactory continuing survey of social intelligence. If your requirements are stricter and you ask about the attention frames (social perceptions) and the perspectives of participants at various stages of a decision process, you are indeed doomed to great disappointment.

Contextualism in Space

Part of the attractiveness of systematic contextual theories is that they are spatially inclusive in reference. This enables the scientific observer to locate his tree in the woods. In principle, it becomes possible to put any specific event in spatial relation to the points of origin of the pattern it exemplifies. Such an ample context enables us to recognize any variations in the pattern that signalize (1) an innovation, or (2) the partial incorporation or rejection of alternative patterns, or the dropping or modification of details of previous forms of the pattern which it most closely approximates. In a given case, doctrines altered by the Supreme Court may be traced as far back as colonial times in this country, pursued across the Atlantic to England, and eventually connected with the doctrines prevailing at a given phase of Roman history. The legal formulae we call the laws of property and contract, for instance, have many lexical continuities and definitional equivalencies in the great digests of the Roman era.

Detailed investigation shows, however, that terms are defined differently, or that equivalent definitions are labeled differently than they once were, owing in some measure to the partial incorporation of local legal doctrines and practices. Further inquiry may show that seeming similarities are utterly superficial. When we examine the context of a decision, it appears that the doctrines are invoked by quite different parties to litigation, on behalf of claims that contrast sharply with the claimants who appeared before the magistrates of imperial Rome. Moreover, the events that precipitated the contemporary controversy are very different. Finally, the predispositions of the decision-makers are in great contrast to those of the magistrates of antiquity, and the outcomes and effects are not the same.

Findings of this kind are in no sense new to the political and legal sciences. What is supplied by a world-inclusive framework (or rather, an inclusive interaction area) is the emphasis on distinctive and important social patterns whose centers of origin, zones, and routes of diffusion and restriction can be sought. In the case of Toynbee, for instance, the significant units to follow are "civilizations." For Marx and Engels, the key units to be identified and examined are social class (class societies such as feudalism and capitalism). These exemplify one of the most significant contributions made by theorists of society—namely, the identification of the principal units whose interactions are regarded as worth pursuing.

Contextualism in Time

Contextual theories are inclusive in time as well as space; they refer to events in the future as well as those in the past of contemporary inquirers. In this connection I distinguish truly "developmental constructs" from other future-reference models. A developmental construct is put forward tentatively, not dogmatically; and it depends upon the critical examination of past trend and distribution data, and upon scientific propositions that have been at least partially confirmed by correlational and experimental methods. Past trends, when extrapolated, characteristically indicate the probability of future conflict in particular zones. Hence, whatever knowledge of the interplay of scientifically investigated factors is at hand must be drawn upon to assess the probable resolution of future conflicts.

In the nineteenth century in particular some of the most inclusive theories of past and future history took their cue from unilinear theories of biological evolution. Sir Henry Maine's characterization of the course of legal evolution as "from status to contract" was widely considered as indicating that in our time the world was moving toward the substitution of deliberately made agreement, in place of the obligations of traditional societies. More comprehensive theories of society, such as those of Spencer and Comte, saw human history as striding away from theocratic or military forms and toward more rational peaceful and permissive institutions.

Strictly speaking, these are not exemplifications of developmental constructs, since they purport to be grounded upon scientifically valid propositions about the determinants of social evolution. We can reject the scientific propositions as doubtful, yet tentatively adopt a Spencerian, Comteian or Marxian model of the distinctive features of future periods. By assigning some estimate of probability to the model, we can then employ it to guide our scientific manpower and resources to the consideration of especially important factors in the social process. I have, for instance, put forward in place of the Marxist construct of the proletarian revolution, followed by the commonwealth of free men, the model of a continuing crisis leading to the universal dominance of new social castes depending upon the control of instruments of coercion. Although this construct was no more than a sketch, it helped to focus some scholars upon civil-military relations and upon the factors affecting the political-military use of the new technology stemming from the recent explosive development of physics and chemistry. Among other things, it has been possible to mobilize a few legal scholars to anticipate, in advance of their appearance, at least some of the problems of weapon surveillance, weather control, the penetration of outer space, automation, artificial insemination, and such.

Functional Reinterpretation of Conventional Meanings

Perhaps it should be made more explicit that a principal scientific task in examining the social process is to confront conventionally defined relationships with the results of functional analysis and research. In conventional terms, we refer to various legal doctrines as "property law," and to various organizations as "business corporations" or "courts." Part of the lure of the qualitative categories of Marxism has been that they encourage intellectuals to discover new linkages between the conventional institutions of a given epoch or locality and the manifold of events in which they are embedded. With the postulation that nineteenth-century Europe was "capitalist" and that the future was to be "socialist," and further that whatever led to socialism was "progressive" and whatever sustained capitalism was "reactionary," the conceptual scene was ready for the inspection of every detail, according to the degree in which the pattern of the future would be expedited and the older pattern weakened.

As the context unfolds, the significance of any specific pattern is likely to change. Thus a standard hypothesis (often a dogmatic conclusion, of course, but not one that necessarily affects the validity of the result) was that parliamentary democracy, which first performed "progressive" functions in the struggle against feudalism, later became perverted to "reactionary" functions by the private owners of the tools of production. It is not necessary to emphasize that research as well as propaganda has been inspired by such hypotheses. In our society some of the fear of empirical social science among businessmen is accounted for by the uneasy sense that there is something in hypotheses of this kind, and hence that such studies may endanger the political support upon which business institutions depend.

I suggest that not only empirical research but also contextual theory suffers from such apprehensiveness. Do we not also discover among social scientists some unwillingness to give prominence to hypotheses that may be widely interpreted as inconsistent with prevailing ideology? Such reluctance would be expected among individuals who were at one time identified with Marxist activities, which they abandoned, largely on grounds of expediency, without thoroughly reorganizing their intellectual position. Here is where preoccupation with partial and highly formal systematizations, or with limited quantitative problems, might be expected to keep vulnerability at a minimum.

My view is that systematic multivalued models of the social process (including of course politico-legal components) are more searching intellectual devices than the earlier socialist models, which, like the capitalist ideology they fought, exaggerated the role of "material" factors. This is not the place to argue the position; I remark only that the multifactor approach to the study of man in society tends by now to have made this proposition more acceptable than formerly.

Our confidence in multivalued "systematic functionalism" must be justified by contrasting it not only with other systematic and single-valued systems, but with unsystematic functionalism. Social anthropologists of the functional school made a great contribution to all the social sciences when they demonstrated the contextual principle. But the research reports prepared under the inspiration of functionalists have lacked comparability. Thus if we learn that the fiesta in one village attracts storytellers and ballad singers who use their talents to provide political news of the outer world, we are justified in saying that one value effect of the fiesta is to provide political enlightenment. But reports on other village fiestas may say nothing about the dissemination of political news. Does this mean that there was none, or that the observer neglected to look for it and note it down?

Systematic Functionalism

What is involved in systematic rather than unsystematic functionalism is suggested by the following questions relating to the legal system of a body politic, studied through time or compared with other systems described the same way. What features of the decision-making and executing process are given legal protection, e.g., are voting frauds illegal in formal prescription and effective fact? What economic practices (institutions) are legally protected, e.g., are business monopolies broken up or regulated? What skill opportunities are legally provided, e.g., are opportunities for vocational training freely offered? What institutions of respect are given the support of the law, e.g., are families assigned to ranks carrying privileges? What institutions of enlightenment are given legal support, e.g., is there freedom of the press from official censorship? What affection institutions receive legal protection, e.g., under what circumstances can marriages be dissolved or otherwise terminated? What rectitude institutions are protected, e.g., are there established churches? What well-being practices are legally sustained, e.g., are basic medical facilities open to all?

The previous questions point to the system of public order, which we define as the patterns of value distribution and the basic institutional practices protected by law. (*Law* refers to the decisions which are supported, if necessary, by severe deprivations directed against challengers.) One goes on to inquire into the degree to which each value is maximized by individuals operating within the constraints of their societal configuration.

If one explores a community in orderly fashion through time, it is possible to show how the conventionally recognized structures change their position in the system of public order, and the degree to which this affects the shaping and sharing of values. The continuing confrontation of conventional conceptions with functional analyses is perhaps the most distinctive contribution of political science, jurisprudence, and other social disciplines.

Some of the protest against "statistical busywork" and other real or imaginary targets seems to stem from a fear that investigations of a contextual kind will become less frequent. But it would be a mistake to imply that contextual theory is independent of "quantification," of statistical investigation. If we turn to some of the famous researches that have performed the confrontation function in political science and law, we immediately see that they have made full use of numerical material. Think of Robert Michels' classic demonstration of how socialist (Social-Democratic) parties in Europe were run year after year by self-perpetuating oligarchies—a proposition supported by data as to the social composition of socialist parties and the class origins of officials—or E. J. Gumbel's comparisons of the treatment by Weimar judges of defendants who were "Rightists" (members of "patriotic societies") or "Leftists" (members of Socialist-Communist organizations), and who were accused of political crimes. The "Leftists" were less often released than the "Rightists," and their sentences were many more years per capita than those of the "Rightists." The scientific proposition that courts tend to *indulge* defendants with whom they identify positively, and to *deprive* defendants with whom they identify negatively, is less important than the report upon the strength of such variables at specific cross sections in time and place. Or recall Charles A. Beard's emphasis upon the economic considerations alleged to have affected the perspectives of our constitutional forefathers. Among the researches that have convincingly emphasized the role of such values as respect, affection, and enlightenment within an industrial society, I mention but one classic, the detailed studies, largely influenced by Elton Mayo, of the output of factory workers, whose production went up so long as they had a congenial human situation and believed that what they were doing would be a pilot model for the reduction of friction in industrial relations.

In our civilization, it appears that the quantitative dimension must be added, even to increase the acceptance among intellectuals, as well as the community at large, of many ethical assertions.

We are coming close in these allusions to the debate over quantification that is so frequently initiated by "humanistic" scholars and that seems so capricious and wrongheaded to scientists. I put to one side the dogmatic assertion that "the human spirit cannot be measured." Social scientists have enough experience to feel sure that they do not have to be perfectionists in order to go a long way toward explaining many of the perspectives presumably included as referents of "human spirit." The "political arithmetic" of the seventeenth century led to the gathering of information regarded as essential for purposes of military policy and revenue. National governments learned to keep or to encourage the keeping of statistics about population, wealth, and trade. Only recently have students of law, politics, and government taken the initiative in gathering information whose principal use is the advancement of knowledge.

Conclusion

The foregoing examination of qualitative-quantitative categories in political and legal analysis has noted some of the connotations attached to the distinction. Practically every connotation makes a valid if limited point, including even those meanings assigned by slogans created for political purposes. Our interest in this colloquium is to deal with quantity and quality as recurring categories in the language of inquiry. Hence we have been most attentive to the distinctions that appear in the formulation of theory, the connecting of theory with observational fields, and the clarification of the interplay between the scientific enterprise and the socio-historical process of which it is a part.

Perhaps the most relevant over-all point relates to the indispensable role performed by the qualitative as well as the quantitative in the tasks of inquiry. In legal and political analysis, for instance, intellectual activities typically move from any given starting point toward more inclusive contexts, or toward a greater specification of acceptable working connections between categories and observational fields. The former is the qualitative direction; the latter, the quantitative.

In many ways the most interesting utterances that make allegedly qualitative or quantitative distinctions refer not to questions of method but to substantive propositions about social change. Admittedly cryptic statements about the transformation of the qualitative into the quantitative, or the reverse, are not amenable to inquiry. But they are challenging if used to stimulate consideration of the circumstances likely to culminate in "cumulative" or "abrupt" politico-legal change.

Some problems of method have not received a generalized solution. I refer to criteria for the degree of quantification to be sought in political and legal researches. Fortunately we are able to obtain the advice of specialists in mathematical statistics in seeking to clarify the cost of achieving in particular problems (or problem categories) a stated level of verification by a stated degree of quantification. Cost, of course, is not solely a matter of man-hours and apparatus; it includes other social values. And cost estimates need to be put in the context of alternative scientific programs.

Creative tension between the qualitative and the quantitative becomes of increasing rather than diminishing importance as we perfect comprehensive and continuing intelligence surveys of world social process, and use more "intensive" tools to disclose the structure of predisposition in every principal context.

The Problem of Quality and Quantity in Economics

WASSILY LEONTIEF

I

THE DIALECTIC juxtaposition of quality and quantity, of uniqueness and repetition, of abstract theory and of concrete description, has from far back been the *leitmotiv* of the running methodological controversy in social science. The nineteenth-century Continental, particularly the German, philosophic tradition supplied the general background for the first stages of this discussion. In economics the issue was originally raised in the full-dress attack mounted in the third quarter of the last century by the so-called German historical school against the then dominant classical theory. It is not surprising that such antitheoretical orientation found no prominent adherents among economists in England, although among the English historians it was quite recently most eloquently espoused by so prominent a scholar as Collingwood.

The emphasis on the singular as against the common, on the organic as against the mechanical, found on the other hand a receptive soil for its development in the economic thought of the United States. Both Thorstein Veblen and Wesley Mitchell, two of the most eminent representatives of indigenous American economic thought, carried on the *Methodenstreit* against quantitative, analytical economics in the grand style of the German historical school. The fact that at the turn of the century the German academic influence in the United States was as strong as and possibly even stronger than the English might be in part responsible for this. In discussing the issue of quality *vs.* quantity, one must keep in mind that it represents only one facet, one stage, of the wider contest between the proponents of concise analytical methods and the defenders of the descriptive individualizing approach.

Among the social sciences, economics came to be considered—and rightly so—a quantitative science par excellence. Quantification in this instance is more than a methodological device employed by the investigator: it is also an object of the inquiry itself. The modern *Homo economicus* may not be the much maligned predatory hedonist, but he certainly is a consciously calculating animal. It is only natural that in explaining his behavior the economist resorts to mathematics, too. However, lest one draw from this the erroneous conclusion that quantitative analysis is restricted to those aspects of the economic process which involve directly observed, consciously (or rather self-consciously) quantifying attitudes, let me emphatically state that this is not the case. Some of the most advanced applications of mathematical methods in economics are found in the fields of general equilibrium analysis and business-cycle theory—both recognized as quasi-mechanical, automatic phenomena formed and operating to a large extent beyond the calculations, outside the control of, and mostly against the wills of, the millions of individuals whom they affect.

II

The raw material from which the economist forms his theory—or if one prefers a more fashionable term, from which he constructs his analytical models—are the millions of various combinations in which specific goods and services are made and used within the economic system he observes. The principal elementary building blocks which he makes up out of his materials are the "production function" and the "utility" or the "consumption function." These he then uses to explain certain manifestations in the behavior of individuals, or of groups of individuals; that is—if one again prefers to use esoteric language—to explain the decisions being taken by the "players" in the vast economic "game."

A production function is a description of the quantitative relationship between the inputs absorbed and the outputs emerging from a particular production process. A baking receipt stating that it takes two pounds of flour, two cups of milk, two eggs, and a quarter of a pound of butter to make two loaves of bread is a typical production function; so is the concise listing of all the various combinations of ore, coke, auxiliary materials, and the labor required to produce various amounts of pig iron.

Let x_1, for example, represent the number of tons of ore, x_2 the number of tons of coke, and x_3, the man-hours of labor used to make y tons of pig iron. The corresponding quantitative input-output relationship can be concisely described by an equation of the form:

$$y = f(x_1, x_2, x_3) \tag{1}$$

the specific shape of the function $f(x_1, x_2, x_3)$ being determined by the given state of technology. The identification of all the variables involved and the definition of the units in which each one of them is measured represent the qualitative side of this concise description of the economically relevant aspects of the ironmaking process; without these specifications the mathematical formula has no empirical meaning.

The production function—with the appropriate identification of variables involved—can be viewed as a relationship derived from a much larger, and qualitatively much richer, set of far more complete descriptions of all the known methods of making iron, or—as the case may be—baking bread. Such a description would for example dwell in full detail on the role played by the temperature maintained in the blast furnace, and the pressure and the oxygen content of air supplied to its top or base. A complete technological production function would thus contain in the parentheses enclosing the predicate of f many such additional variables not included in its abbreviated version used in equation (1). The economist eliminates them and thus reduces the qualitative complexity (the dimensionality) of the material with which he will have to deal from then on. He retains only those variables the magnitudes of which affect *directly* either the costs incurred in, or the revenue received from, the operation of the production process he describes. Since ore, coke, and labor, as well as pig iron itelf, have positive prices, the change in the magnitude of any one of these variables will directly affect the costs incurred in (or the revenue received from) the ironmaking process. Thus, if any one of these variables were omitted from the production function, the economist would be unable to identify the profit-maximizing input-output combination which he assumes will be in fact maintained by the producer whose actions he sets out to explain.

It is of course true that variations in the amount of air supplied under pressure to the furnace, or changes in its internal operating temperature, would affect the efficiency and consequently the profitability of the entire process as well. Such "nonpriced" variables, however, exert their influence on costs or revenue only indirectly, through modifying the quantitative relationships between the "priced" factors: A change in the supply of air or in the furnace temperature would, for example, increase or decrease the pig-iron yield obtained from given fixed amounts of ore, coke, and labor, or affect the amount of coke required to produce a fixed amount of pig iron with given quantities of ore and labor. As a matter of fact, the profit-maximizing producer can be expected to adjust the magnitudes of all the nonpriced variables in such a way as to attain an efficient relationship between the quantities of the priced variables. On the assumption that he actually does so, the economist proceeds to explain the producer's action in terms of a reduced production function; that is, a production function which describes not all the possible combinations of all the technologically relevant variables, but only certain preselected efficient relationships between the priced variables.

It is worth noting that no irreparable damage is caused if, by oversight or for some other reason, the economist's condensed production function did contain some of the extra technological variables. It could still be used to explain correctly the producer's profit-maximizing behavior; except that the explanation (i.e., the calculations) would have to be carried out in a larger number of dimensions than is absolutely necessary.

III

Another simpler and fundamentally much more general device which the economist uses to reduce the number of qualitative distinctions required for the explanation of observed facts is the method of formal substitution.

Let us enlarge the scope of the previous example by including in it the ore-mining and the coke-making sectors of the economy along with the blast-furnace industry itself. This can be done by setting up two additional production functions. In the description of mining operations, the variable x_1 representing (as it did before) the quantity of ore will appear on the left-hand side of the equation as the output; on its right-hand side, under the function sign ϕ—representing the appropriate reduced technical relationship—this equation will contain new input variables: say, z_1 = the tonnage or the cubic yards of ore-bearing deposits, z_2 = the number of kilowatt hours of electric power, and z_3 = man-years of miners' work:

$$x_1 = \phi\ (z_1, z_2, z_3) \tag{2}$$

Similarly, another equation describing the production of coke shows its quantity, x_2, as related to the quantities of the inputs, coal, v_1, and labor, v_2:

$$x_2 = \theta\ (v_1, v_2) \tag{3}$$

In widening the scope of the inquiry, we have thus introduced five new qualitatively distinct variables and two additional functional relationships. But having made this step forward, we can now take a half-step back. Let us substitute for the variables x_1 and x_2 as they appear on the right-hand side of equation (1) their production functions presented in equations (2) and (3). Thus we obtain a new, enlarged production function for pig iron:

$$y = f\ [\phi\ (z_1, z_2, z_3),\ \theta\ (v_1, v_2),\ x_3] \tag{4}$$

This function is more comprehensive than the first insofar as it reaches back behind the iron-smelting process and covers two other sectors of the economy, one engaged in the mining of ore (x_1), and the other in the making of coke (x_2). These two variables are, however, not entered explicitly on the right-hand side of the enlarged equation. Instead, that side shows the inputs used by the ore-mining and coke-making industries, respectively. Of the nine variables appearing in the first three equations, the two mentioned above have been eliminated in the last, without making our analysis less concise. The purpose of this example is to show that the formal operation of algebraic substitution, when used in analysis of real (i.e., observable) phenomena, permits us to describe them with fewer qualitative terms.

IV

Turning to the utility function, we again meet the substitution method—but used in reverse. In analyzing the behavior of consumers, the economist assigns to this function a role similar to that which he gives to the production function in the description and explanation of the behavior of producers. The inputs consist now, not of ore and coke, but of such consumers' goods as bread and shoes; the output is not pig iron but utility. But what is utility, how can it be measured, does it exist at all? Strangely enough, the economists began to ask themselves these questions only relatively recently. Before that, they spoke of satisfaction or utility as if it were an object with as distinct, immediately observable qualities as steel or bread. However, as soon as the pedantic Edgeworth and the skeptical Pareto expressed their doubts on that score, a lively, not to say violent, discussion ensued which has not subsided yet. Some theorists maintain that utility exists and can indeed be measured like steel or bread, although the yardsticks applied to different persons and the resulting measurements can in no way be compared with one another. Others deny the possibility of any such cardinal measurement, even for a single person; they assert that the amounts of utility from which an individual has opportunity to choose can be compared with one another only ordinally: As in the case of pain, one does not know how much one has of it, but only feels that it is becoming more or less intense. Finally, there are theorists who do not care whether utility exists and is measurable or not. They say that the behavior of a consumer (for example, the change in the quantities of various goods he buys and in the amount of work he will do to earn the income with which to pay for them) can be explained without recourse to a variable called utility.

There is an obvious analogy between the problem of the existence or nonexistence of utility and of its explanatory use, and the question of whether one can or should substitute the intermediate variables, x_1 and x_2, which came up before when we discussed the problem of compounding the interrelated production functions for pig iron, ore, and coke. Imagine a situation in which the inputs and outputs accessible to direct observation by the economist are only those described by the variables shown in the compound production function (4).

This means that his empirical data permit him to establish a valid quantitative relationship between the amounts of ore-bearing land (z_1), electric power (z_2), and labor (z_3) absorbed in mining operations; the quantities of coal (v_1) and labor (v_2) used for making coke; and the amount of blast-furnace-tending labor (x_3) on the one hand; and on the other the quantity of pig-iron (y) emerging at the end of the entire combined operation. This information will obviously permit him to construct and use for further analytical purposes the integrated over-all production equation (4); such factual information, however, will not be sufficient to enable our economist to reconstruct each one of its component parts, that is, the three production functions describing separately the pig-iron-smelting process and the processes of mining ore and of making coke. Neither his immediate empirical evidence nor his theoretical model will contain any reference whatsoever to either the qualities or quantities of such objects as ore or coke.

This could not, however, prevent our investigator from embarking on what will appear to be an arbitrary theoretical construction of the three interrelated intermediate functions containing two new "artificial" variables, x_1 and x_2. Not only their dimensions (i.e., their qualitative properties) but even their very existence would obviously depend in this case only on circumstantial evidence combined with certain essentially arbitrary a priori assumptions. The analytical purpose of introducing these two additional variables would be to provide a means of breaking down one complicated quantitative relationship into three simpler ones. If numerical manipulations are involved, a theoretical reformulation of this kind often leads to considerable simplification of the computational procedure.

Returning to the problem of the existence (if one assumes that it does exist) of alternative measures of utility, we can now see by analogy that it is essentially a question of introduction or omission of an auxiliary variable and of a corresponding reformulation of a given system of theoretical relationships.

V

The delicate interplay between direct observation and analytical construction has been dramatically illuminated by the following curious incident from the recent history of economic thought. Twenty years ago a prominent Soviet Russian mathematician, Professor L. V. Kantorovich, published a paper in which he developed a new approach to production planning. The problem he set out to solve was essentially one of choosing among several technologically possible methods of producing a given goods that which would maximize its output. In particular he considered cases in which each one of the available alternative methods could be described as a specific combination of the amounts of various factors required to produce a unit of the finished goods and in which the total available quantities of all factors were fixed. In our previous example, one method would, for instance, require a ton of pig iron; another, one and a quarter tons of ore, but only two and a half tons of coke and one and three-quarters man-hours of labor; and so on. Given a total supply, say, of six hundred thousand tons of ore, fifteen thousand tons of coke, and eleven thousand man-hours, what method or what combination of methods would enable us to produce the largest possible amount of pig iron? This was Kantorovich's question.

He found that the calculation of a correct answer—if the number of distinct possible input combinations and the number of inputs involved is fairly large—is greatly facilitated if one introduces certain auxiliary variables which he called "allocation coefficients," represented in his theoretical formulae by the symbols $\lambda_1, \lambda_2, \ldots \lambda_n$.

At the time of publication, Kantorovich's paper apparently found little response among Russian economists and none among the practical planners. It did not reach the West when published in 1939; the hot war and the subsequent cold war intervened, so that Western economists had the opportunity of acquainting themselves with its contents only a short time ago. They were surprised to find that Kantorovich's "allocation coefficients" were actually the prices of the individual goods and services, which appeared as inputs in his production functions. That is, the quantitative relationship established by Kantorovich between these λ_1's on the one hand and the shapes of his production functions and the given total amounts of the various inputs on the other, was exactly the same as is used in Western economic theory to explain the determination of factor prices in a competitive economy.

This theory in its modern version views the entire national economy as a kind of gigantic computer. Propelled by the profit-maximization motive and other similar forces, it automatically solves the problem of the efficient allocation of all available resources. The computational technique which this natural machine employs to arrive at correct answers is the so-called iterative procedure, that is, the method of step-by-step approximation through trial and error.

For Western economists, prices are elements of the observed reality, as real as are the tangible physical properties of various goods. The objects of Kantorovich's analysis were only these physical quantities and the technical relations between them. There is good reason to believe that in the context of the planning problem which he intended to solve, the actual existence of observable prices was not taken into account by him at all. Facing a well-defined empirical problem, he was led by the internal logic of the theoretical argument, combined with considerations of computational convenience, to the artificial construction of peculiar measurable qualities which under somewhat different conditions actually happen to exist. The Western theory of linear programming, which Kantorovich's original contribution has anticipated in part, uses the term "shadow prices." The relationship between observed and constructed qualities and quantities in modern science, indeed, reminds one of a Pirandello play.

VI

The conceptual apparatus of modern economics described above has a rather fragile but at the same time precisely balanced structure. It contains variables which represent directly observed facts; by this I mean facts which were more often observed by someone else rather than the economist himself, and were usually described in ordinary, everyday language or in the technical language, not of economics, but of some other discipline. These variables make up the cutting edge of the analytical tool without which it could have no operational significance. As we have seen, this tool also contains in its inner works auxiliary concepts of a rather artificial kind. Both qualitatively and quantitatively the two types of variables are mutually aligned, like gears in a well-made clock. This does not mean that the qualitative characteristics of the artificial variables are similar to those of the variables belonging to the more realistic group. On the contrary, it is precisely their different qualitative make-up on which the effective analytic combination of the two kinds of variables depends.

The introductory paragraphs of this essay contained a reference to Wesley Mitchell as representative of a major antitheoretical trend in American economic thought. While criticizing the erection of elaborate theoretical models, he proposed to rely on direct observation not based on any preconceived notions, and in particular advocated massive measurement of the observed facts. To Mitchell, to his pupils, and to his successors, this country owes the large-scale development of descriptive economic statistics without which not only modern economics but many of the modern economic institutions could not possibly exist.

While they are suspicious of theoretical speculation, the proponents of this self-professed positivistic approach nevertheless make up new scientific concepts or at least adopt some of those already in use. Typical examples are the regularly published figures of the "U.S. national income," of the "U.S. output of consumers' goods," and the "price level of agricultural products." None of these terms refers to a concrete object familiar to the direct participants in daily practical economic transactions. Each one refers, however, to a group of such objects defined in a rather simple, not to say simple-minded, way. The "output of consumers' goods" is obviously meant to be the combined total of the measured outputs of bread, shoes, men's suits, TV sets, and so on; the "average price level of agricultural products," the average price of wheat, cotton, oranges, meat, etc. The objects in each group have some property in common—that of being used by consumers or being prices of all products of agricultural enterprise—but they differ from one another in many of their qualities, too. In no case does there exist a common unit which can be unambiguously used to measure the magnitude of all the individual members of each group before one proceeds to sum them up or to average them out. The operation of determining the magnitude of such artificial aggregative objects—the economic statistician calls them index numbers—involves, in other words, adding pounds or tons of steel and yards or meters of cloth. The final result thus necessarily depends on the arbitrary choice of units in which one measures the magnitude of each one of the component parts.

If one speaks of the "output of consumers' goods" instead of the outputs of bread, shoes, and books, or of the "price of agricultural commodities" instead of the price of wheat, the entire economic system can indeed be described in fewer words. However, the reduction in qualitative variety is attained at the cost of ever increasing quantitative indeterminacy; as we have seen, the more general the contents of an index number, the more vague and arbitrary will its measure be. This puts strict upper limits on the effectiveness of verbal generalization—and on that of the corresponding quantitative procedure of averaging or of aggregating—as a tool of economic research. On the lower levels of scientific inquiry its use of course cannot possibly be avoided. When one speaks in general of "appliances" instead of "consumers' durables," one excludes automobiles but leaves unspecified whether one has in mind refrigerators, washing machines, or TV sets; and when one speaks of refrigerators, one still omits the distinction between those run by electricity and those operated by gas. Only an ideal theoretical system could take in all observable distinctions and explain them to the last detail. At any given stage of its development, economic analysis—like theoretical analysis in any other empirical discipline—can operate effectively on a certain level of qualitative differentiation, but not further down. However, the cutoff point below which the economist has to ignore qualitative distinctions (since he cannot explain them) can be expected to shift downward.

Both the theoretical analyst and the antitheoretical empiricist must rely on crude verbal generalization as the only means they can begin with to reduce to manageable proportions the seemingly unfathomable variety of the immediately observed facts. The difference between the two shows up in what they do next. The theorist sets out to develop generalizations of a more complex and systematic kind, with which he expects first of all to master the obvious qualitative distinctions preserved at the first descriptive stage. He furthermore proceeds to recover and to incorporate into his analytical system successive layers of finer differences which were neglected or suppressed in the original verbal purge.

The empiricist, to the extent to which he wants to generalize at all, prefers to follow the first verbal step with a second, third, and so on. The entire sequence involves thus nothing more than omitting details, averaging, and aggregating. In following this apparently simple and safe procedure, the opponent of theoretical speculation soon finds himself facing unexpectedly the highly speculative and—what is worse—essentially unsolvable problems of so-called index-number theory. He winds up either with a system of quantitatively well-defined relationships between qualitatively ill-defined variables or with a set of quantitatively indeterminate—or at least loosely described—relationships between sharply defined variables.

The process of the gradual deepening and expansion of economic inquiry naturally brings it into closer contact with adjoining fields. Modern economics has established with technical-engineering disciplines a close cooperative relationship based on an effective division of labor. However, its borders with other social sciences are still very little explored, and its relations with them are marked not so much by active cooperation as by jurisdictional disputes in which each side raises claims on some outlying territories which with their present analytical resources neither can in fact occupy or hold. Two fields of scientific inquiry can be interconnected effectively only through a clear conceptual overlap. Moreover, the overlapping (that is, the common) concepts must have proven their internal operational effectiveness separately in each one of the adjoining disciplines. If these basic conditions are not satisfied, interdisciplinary committees and interdisciplinary negotiation can yield no more than an exchange of reciprocal propaganda claims.

Quantification in Economics: Its History*

JOSEPH J. SPENGLER

The more advanced the sciences have become, the more they have tended to enter the domain of mathematics, which is a sort of center towards which they converge.

Adolphe Quételet, *Instructiones populaires*, p. 230

The nineteenth century has in great measure achieved qualitative analysis in economics. . . . It has felt the necessity for quantitative analysis; . . . but the achievement itself stands over for you.

A. Marshall, in an address to the Cambridge Economic Club, 1896

THIS PAPER deals with the introduction of quantification into economics, until recently a moral science avowedly concerned with questions of policy.[1] The period covered ends with World War I because it is not possible, in a short essay, to deal effectively with the extensive progress made in statistical method, mathematical economics, and econometrics since 1920. My main concern is to trace historically the quantification of economic science and to isolate some of the circumstances that conditioned this quantification—among them, the changing character of economics, variation in the economic role of the state, progress in mathematics, and examples furnished by other disciplines. Only incidental attention is given to discovering whether the quantification of economic science passed through stages similar to those that supposedly accompanied its introduction into medicine and some of the life sciences.[2] No attempt is made to determine the degree to which the introduction of quantitative methods was affected by the values, norms, and modes of organization present in economic science and its propagation.[3]

* I am indebted to the Ford and Rockefeller foundations for assistance.

Quantification in economics has assumed two forms which, though originally quite distinct, now tend to merge, particularly when the nature of the problem conduces to such merging. Under one heading may be grouped the assembly of unidimensional numerical indicators of economic and/or economically oriented phenomena (e.g., crude price data, census returns), their transformation into multidimensional indicators or into simple aggregative indices, and their interpretation and analysis with the object of discovering trends, concurrence, sequence, covariation, patterns of movement, etc. Under the other heading may be included hypothetical and/or mathematical models, which are designed to incorporate one or more propositions and, usually, also to represent, in a simplified manner, certain interrelations supposed to exist in some underlying sector of economic reality.[4]

Introduction

The science of economics did not assume a stable form until the eighteenth century, long after quantitative data had begun to be gathered and some time after what then passed for "statistics," together with as yet unrelated rudiments of mathematical statistics, had begun to develop. Economics, of course, had already begun to come into being in the later Middle Ages and to take shape during the Age of Mercantilism, in the course of which inferences began to be drawn from data that were both quantitative and of economic significance. But it remained for Quesnay and Smith, together with Cantillon, Hume, and Steuart, to establish economics as the first of the social sciences. Of these individuals, however, only the first two, though founders of somewhat different schools, made considerable use of quantitative approaches. The succeeding nineteenth century witnessed the establishment of a number of schools—the classical, the Austrian, the mathematical, the historical, the Marxian, and the neoclassical—each of which assigned a somewhat unique scope and content to economics and sought answers to a somewhat unique set of questions. Consequently, these schools differed with respect to the role assigned to quantitative method. This role became much greater in the second quarter of the twentieth century, with the rise of macroeconomics and a consequent increase in emphasis on the pursuit of public policies based upon the state of economic indicators and their supposed quantitative interrelationships. The recrudescence of interest in economic growth, beginning after World War I and in part an outcome of trade-cycle studies, has greatly intensified quantitative study of the past.

Although the weight assigned quantitative methods by any given school was conditioned by the scope which it assigned to economics and by the importance which it attributed to the economic role of the state, it was also affected by this kind of statistical information available and accessible, and by the current degree of development of statistical and related mathematical techniques, together with their applicability in conformity with received canons of scientific inquiry. Record-keeping had been considered important in ancient times, both by businessmen and firms interested in pursuing profitable courses of action and by administrative branches of governments—even of those better remembered for their waste than for their husbandry of surplus value—concerned with the collection or the disbursement of revenues. Such records became increasingly important as trade began to expand in Western Europe after the tenth century, with the result that the science of accounting underwent considerable improvement, particularly in its applications to private activities.[5] Even so, the data of firms did not become significantly available for study until, or after, the late nineteenth century. There were available, however, data relating to prices, wages, debt, revenue, customs returns, and, above all, population, of great interest to analysts so long as they looked upon growth of the labor force as the principal source of increase in aggregate national income.[6] Before the nineteenth century, nonetheless, shortages of data greatly restricted what economists might do, though but few made effective use of what was available. In the nineteenth century, however, both data and the uses made of data improved, each type of progress reinforcing the other. The nineteenth century, moreover, witnessed the initial discovery and frequently the introduction into use, generally after marked delay, of most of the statistical techniques that were known before World War I.

Much of what initially passed for statistics, including that from which the subject got its name, had little to do with quantities or with economics. It received great stimulus, nonetheless, from a circumstance that had several times stimulated the quantification of economics, namely, an intensification of the economic role of the state, together with recognition that effective performance of this role calls for suitable data and data-processing. The mid-nineteenth century witnessed a marked increase in emphasis upon what was then called statistics, the content of which had been foreshadowed a century earlier. By that time the doctrine of *raison d'état* had widespread currency, especially in national states bent upon expansion, and finance and administration were beginning to be looked upon as sciences, at least by the cameralists and their sympathizers.[7] "Statistics," as conceived in sixteenth-century Italy and as subsequently developed in the lectures of Herman Conring (1606–81) and his successors, and in the works of Gottfried Achenwall (1719–72) and his followers, consisted largely of descriptions of the nations of Europe and of their legal and other institutions, together with estimates of their manpower, industry, resources, etc. It was far more descriptive than numerical, and it continued to be so in Germany in the early part of the nineteenth century, though not in England, France, or Italy, where the numerical side received greater emphasis.[8] When contemporaries of the exponents of "Staatenkunde"[9] resorted to tabular arrangements and to increasingly numerical materials around 1800, the latter took strong exceptions thereto.[10] Yet even Quételet, despite his concern to join probability theory with political arithmetic, gave some support to the approach of Achenwall.[11] Furthermore, although the conception of statistics as essentially a body of state-oriented descriptive data died out, particularly with the rise of specialized social sciences (e.g., political economy, geography), the conception of statistics as primarily a body of methods and/or of mathematical techniques was slow to develop despite the progress made in mathematical statistics. Methodological emphasis was upon the orderly presentation and the inductive interpretation of quantitative matter relating to man, even in "the era of enthusiasm" (1830–49) which witnessed the establishment of various statistical societies.[12] Empirical emphasis remained upon the accumulation and organization of numerical data, with additions to utilizable quantitative knowledge as perhaps the main objective. Not until late in the nineteenth century were these emphases substantially changed. Nor did this change in emphasis go unchallenged.[13]

The Development of Statistical Techniques

The quantification of economics has been greatly influenced, in the longer run, by several forces external to economics—namely, improvements in mathematics and in mathematical statistics, itself a (sometimes neglected) branch of mathematics, and in the quantity and quality of statistical information being assembled. In this section, I deal with the discovery of relevant statistical concepts and methods and with the degree to which these instruments found their way into late nineteenth-century and early twentieth-century textbooks on statistics for economists.[14] The application of mathematics to the definition, or the resolution, of questions of the sort dealt with in "economic theory" is summarized below in the section dealing with mathematical economics.

Of historically prior importance is the theory of probability and the discovery of the normal curve. The foundations of probability theory were laid in the seventeenth century, long before economics was thought of as a science; it was initially applied to problems connected with games of chance and with pricing approximations to annuities. In J. Bernoulli's *Ars Conjectandi* (1713), it was suggested that his theory could be applied to moral, civil, and economic affairs, an application that was often touched upon in later works (e.g., of Laplace).[15] A. Demoivre discovered the normal curve in 1733, announced a formula for it, and applied close approximations to what were later called standard deviation and probable error.[16] Demoivre's work attracted no attention, however, and other less satisfactory distributions of chance errors were proposed.[17] In the very early nineteenth century, however, as a result of the work of Laplace and Gauss and of Legendre on least squares (1805), a foundation was "laid for a theory of errors of observation," and its formula was established. The term *probable error* was used by F. W. Bessel in 1815. In 1832 J. F. Encke, resting upon the work of his teacher, Gauss, gave formulas for computing a standard deviation, various standard and probable errors, etc.[18] In sum, by 1812 the theory of probability (including the normal curve) had been well established, and by 1820–30 "the law of errors had come into very general use among astronomers and physicists."[19] It should be noted that the "discovery" of this law resulted from a preoccupation with the "derivation of infinite series which facilitate computations for astronomy and navigation," and that the law was supposed to describe man's fallibility as an observer. In 1837 S. D. Poisson dispensed with the Gaussian assumption of equal *a priori* probabilities and developed a somewhat different curve of distribution, which, because it became symmetrical as the number of items increased, he believed to be an expression of the law of great numbers.[20]

Extension of the law of error and of the law of great numbers to social phenomena was largely the work of the mathematician and astronomer, A. Quételet (1796–1874), who believed that statistical methods adapted to astronomy and the estimation of errors of observation were equally applicable to the study of social phenomena and of man's attributes. His study of the distribution of human stature eventually led him to conclude that the average man, the man with average physical and moral attributes, is the basic type, from which other types are deviations[21] and about which individuals are normally distributed.

Apparently, Quételet's inference that the regularities supposedly characteristic of man's moral behavior approximate social laws did not greatly and directly affect the introduction of quantitative methods into economics, perhaps because he held society largely responsible for the moral behavior of its members and allowed little scope for individual freedom.[22] He may, however, have affected this introduction indirectly, by incorrectly inferring that a social (or an economic) universe is of the same order as that universe of a supposed infinity of measurements which underlies the law of error. He seems to have stimulated Francis Galton and Karl Pearson, who contributed greatly to the development and use of the statistical techniques that were taken over by economists early in the present century.[23] He may also have indirectly stimulated those who later accommodated the role of the normal curve in statistical theory to the fact that in nature there are distributions other than those represented by the curve of error. For it was soon discovered that sources of variation other than errors of observation gave rise to various types of distribution; and W. Lexis, one of the first to observe this, even presented methods (in the late 1870's) for estimating the degree of noncorrespondence between actual distributions and the distribution of errors.[24]

The last twenty to twenty-five years of the nineteenth century and the first decade of the present century witnessed the advent of a new era in statistical theory and the gradual adaptation of the resulting improvements to the analysis of economic problems.[25] The role of the probability calculus, together with normal-curve and other distribution equations and derivative measures of central tendency and dispersion, was clarified and adjusted to the needs of the empirical investigator. Many of these developments originated in England, where they were fed by Galton's interest in genetics, by Pearson's concern to establish statistical inquiry on a theoretically tenable basis, and by Edgeworth's interest in exploring the "conceptions underlying the law of error," in connecting measures of dispersion with a law of error, in finding the causes underlying distributions found in nature, and in accommodating statistical theory to economic analysis.[26]

Bowley, Yule, Weldon, and others played an important role in diffusing and further advancing the newer methods, which spread to Scandinavia, Italy, and other countries where the approach was not of the highly empirical sort favored by Mayr.[27] Edgeworth, Galton, Fechner, and others dealt with the properties of various means, with indices of dispersion, and with the suitability of various means to particular situations, a subject to which Jevons had given attention as early as the 1860's.[28] Pearson, having arrived in the 1890's at formulas for computing moments and their errors, utilized the moments, much as T. N. Thiele utilized semi-invariants, to fit curves of the sort to which the older method of least squares was less applicable.[29] With the development of interest in trends and comparisons, attention was directed to the removal of seasonal and cyclical variation,[30] as, with the rise of correlation analysis, it was directed to the isolation of correlatable variations from trends.[31] There is occasional reference in articles cited below to problems of smoothing curves and removing types of variations.[32] It was not, however, until after 1914 that periodigrams and harmonic analysis were frequently applied in the investigation of types of fluctuations.[33] Sampling was slow to come into use, despite its availability.[34]

Although Galton hit upon the idea of correlation as early as 1877, and it had been implied by A. Bravais in 1846, correlation techniques applicable to two or more variables were not well described until the 1890's.[35] Rank correlation was expounded in 1904, and Yule's conception of association and contingency in 1900.[36] Correlation techniques were slow to be adopted by economists, however, even though Yule early used the technique to correct mistaken conclusions regarding the causes of pauperism.[37] R. H. Hooker correlated deviations from a moving average of the marriage rate with those from both lagged and unlagged moving averages of indices of trade.[38] Hooker also undertook, through the use of correlation analysis, to discover how closely prices in different markets were associated.[39] J. P. Norton correlated variations in discount rates with variations in reserve-deposit ratios in 1901, and A. Lee correlated imports and employment.[40] Except for a few additional studies, some of which are reported in the section on schools of economic theory and methods, below, there does not seem to have been much application of correlation to economic problems before 1917.

A number of leading economists, most of whom were more interested in the applications of statistics than in its methodological development, discussed the role and use of graphs in the closing third of the nineteenth century.[41] W. S. Jevons, who stressed the usefulness of rectangular coordinate paper,[42] was the first economist to use a semilogarithmic grid when analyzing economic data.[43] In 1885 E. Levasseur discussed a variety of methods of graphic presentation, but not the use of log-log and arith-log grids. A. Marshall did not endorse the use of these grids, though he dealt with rate of growth[44]; nor did A. W. Flux, in an article on "Graphic Method" in which he treated even stereograms and contour lines.[45] As late as 1917, despite what had been written, Irving Fisher reported that the arith-log chart remained little known.[46]

Of the indicators of economic change, index numbers were the first to command economists' attention, and interest in them increased markedly in the latter half of the nineteenth century. Only indices having to do with prices and with the movement of real wages were treated prior to the closing years of the century, however. Interest in measures of this sort antedated 1800, with Adam Smith and others seeking a measure of "value," and with at least five authors making use of price averages. A few authors made use of price indices during the period from 1800 to 1850, among them Scrope's tabular standard, and a greater number from 1850 to 1880 with some reflecting the growing interest in measures of central tendency.[47]

By 1880, use had been made of arithmetic, geometric, and harmonic averages of prices; of the Laspeyres base-period and the Paasche later-period weighted index numbers; and of the Drobisch double-weighted type.[48] After 1880, index numbers began to be supplied for most countries, and exploration of the theory underlying index-number construction was intensified. Between 1880 and 1900, important contributions were made by Edgeworth, W. Lexis, L. Walras, J. Lehr, A. Sauerbeck, J. S. Nicholson, A. Marshall, H. Westergaard, R. Zuckerkandl, and others;[49] and price indices began to appear in articles in economic periodicals. Between 1900 and 1917, indices appeared more frequently in journal articles, and much attention was given to problems of averaging, weighting, etc., with I. Fisher, W. C. Mitchell, C. M. Walsh, A. W. Flux, Edgeworth, A. A. Young, A. C. Pigou, and others making important contributions. Although statisticians did a great deal of work on index numbers, "the decisive impulses and ideas" continued to come,[50] as in earlier periods, "from economic theorists."[51]

Whereas interest in wage and real-wage movements paralleled that in price indices and the value of money, interest in other indices did not develop until the present century. Interest in wage movements directed attention to the fact that the price indices used to translate money wages into real terms must fit the situation under analysis.[52] In the closing decade of the century, effective work on the measurement of unemployment began to be undertaken.[53] Weighted indices of production were even slower to develop; until after World War I, movements of such recorded single-product totals as coal production, or such multiple-component aggregates as tax revenue or foreign trade or components thereof, were counted on to represent change.[54] Indicative of the composite series developed right after the war, together with components, is that described in the new *Review of Economic Statistics.*[55]

There is little evidence that, before 1917, growth curves occupied a significant place in the apparatus of users of quantitative method in economics.[56] Interest in trends was confined largely to the discovery and correlation of deviations from trends, or to finding relatively short cycle-free movements. Until near the close of the nineteenth century, *ad hoc* population projections continued to be made, particularly for New World countries and potential-enemy countries; and there was recurrent reference to limitations on the continuing growth of the food supply. Use was seldom made, however, of empirically fitted curves,[57] or of curves that incorporated a rational theory based on fundamental presuppositions. Instead, it was customary to suppose that a certain rate of growth would obtain for a time and would then be replaced, for some period, by another and usually lower rate. P. F. Verhulst's logistic curve, expounded in papers between 1838 and 1847, was soon forgotten, to be rediscovered only in 1918-20, when apprehension about prospective overpopulation was increasing.[58] Nor was there recourse to other asymptotic growth curves (e.g., Galton's ogive, the Gompertz curve, the modified exponential); these came into use after World War I.[59] Usually, improvements were reported in noncurvilinear form.[60]

In and after the closing decade of the nineteenth century, new measures of the distribution of wealth and income came into use. Their formulation was prompted by interest in whether "inequality" was increasing or decreasing, together with the belief of some that measures of dispersion around averages provided incomplete answers. Pareto's log-log curve (first published in 1895), the first of these measures, commanded attention in Italy among Pareto's disciples, and elsewhere among both his followers and his critics, in part because Pareto inferred that the comparative invariance of the slope of the curve indicated the distribution of income to be quite stable. Less than a decade later, M. O. Lorenz published the curve bearing his name, with cumulative percentages of income recipients expressed in arithmetic terms. Several years later, C. Gini began to develop an index resembling Lorenz's and a log-log type of curve, an element (i.e., the index of concentration) that could be expressed in terms of the slope of Pareto's curve.[61] G. P. Watkins used a log-log type of distribution that somewhat resembled Pareto's curve and inferred that wealth was becoming more concentrated in the

West.[62] W. M. Persons, having noted defects in other methods (e.g., those of Pareto, Lorenz, and Watkins), endorsed the coefficient of variation.[63] Others approved Bowley's use of quartiles to measure dispersion.[64]

The progress in statistical method during the last decade of the nineteenth century is suggested by a comparison of Bowley's *Elements* (1901) with manuals published a few years earlier. Bowley dealt with averages (other than the harmonic), measures of dispersion, the graphic method, moving averages, elimination of seasonality, arith-log curves, error, index numbers, interpolation and curve fitting, probability, use of the curve of error, the stability of small numbers, samples, and correlation. R. M. Smith's *Statistics and Economics*[65] consisted primarily of demographic and economic statistics, a comparison of statistical and historical methods, a contrast of the English view that statistics could merely aid science, and a discussion of "freedom of the will." M. Block included in his treatise considerable demographic matter, a historical account, a description of statistical organizations, and a discussion of theory that embraced little method other than probability and the life table.[66] Meitzen treated units and processes of enumeration, together with the discovery of causal connections through study of series and graphs. He touched upon probability and the regularity of phenomena, emphasized the examination of returns and the presentation of results, but included nothing on measures, their derivation and uses, their implications, etc.[67] In contrast with Block, Meitzen, and statisticians of similar orientation, A. Cabaglio dealt effectively with averages, measures of dispersion, error, etc., as well as with the use of graphs.[68]

It may be said that statistics, conceived as a body of tools applicable in economics as in other sciences, did not begin its ascendance until early in the present century.[69] Bowley's *Elements* was the first English manual to incorporate this approach, and W. I. King's *The Elements of Statistical Methods* (1912) the first American.[70] Until around 1900 Edgeworth's paper, "Methods of Statistics," remained the "only" source "readily available" to economists interested in using applicable mathematical methods.[71] Although statistics was winning a place in the university curriculum in the 1890's, it did not, in the form taught, usually incorporate the tool approach until the present century.[72] The recency of the wide-scale employment of quantitative methods in economics is suggested by the fact that 25 to 35 years ago the need for more quantitative analysis was still being urged.[73]

Quantitative Method in Economics before 1800

This section is devoted primarily to the role of quantification in economics before it was given that classical form which directly, or through the medium of its critics, so largely shaped the response of nineteenth-century economists to the use of quantitative methods. The role of quantification was envisaged somewhat differently by the main precursors (F. Quesnay, A. Smith, T. R. Malthus) of formal political economy and population theory than by the political arithmeticians. My discussion is limited essentially to pre-1800 political arithmeticians. Their approach to the use of number was shared in some measure, however, by various writers of the following century and a half (e.g., M. G. Mulhall, David Wells, Carl Snyder), and their sentiments at times remind the reader of sentiments of present-day students of economic growth.

POLITICAL ARITHMETICIANS

The political arithmeticians were concerned with both demographic matters and politico-economic questions. They reflected the late seventeenth-century interest in experimental science and brought about improvement in and emphasis on the use of income and other numerical data to support arguments. My concern being with their use of quantitative economic data, I shall confine my attention largely to English exemplars, to the neglect of Continental economists (e.g., Vauban, Forbonnais, Dupré, de Saint Maur) and demographers with economic interests.[74] The work of Graunt, Jan de Witt (1625–72), and others on mortality and its laws quickly proved of economic importance, however, because it made possible a theory of annuities at a time when tontines and annuities were used as forms of public debt; it also contributed, along with the development of probability theory, to the establishment of insurance.[75] Graunt's discovery of regularity and uniformity in the vital phenomena he studied, because of its influence on later demographic writers and because it opened the way for both the discovery and the study of "uniformities in many social or volitional phenomena,"[76] must have helped generate the post-1800 opinion that regularity and uniformity also characterized economic phenomena.[77] His findings relating to population growth were significant because they placed its study, then as now deemed important, upon a firm numerical basis.

Petty, Graunt's contemporary and a disciple of Francis Bacon, made extensive use of quantitative matter and calculation in both his economic and his demographic work, anticipating the view that in economics statistical investigation might take the place of experimentation, but restricting his inquiries to phenomena that supposedly were constant rather than mutable.[78] From these inquiries he derived empirical propositions (e.g., that connecting rent and population, or that asserting the superiority of manufacture and commerce to husbandry);[79] estimates of wealth, income, amount of money required, etc.;[80] a supposed "par" between land and labor;[81] and guidance for national economic policy—a concern which prompted many of his inquiries.[82] He did not, however, derive a conception of statistics as a set of techniques for investigating mass phenomena.

Of the estimates of a nation's income undertaken before the nineteenth century, the ablest is that of Gregory King, who probably was also the first to state, in what amounts to schedule form, the demand for a product (corn).[83] This estimate did not appear in full until 1802, though much of it was presented by Davenant,[84] who found King's findings superior to Petty's. King's estimates "gives a useful framework of analysis for the English economy at the end of the seventeenth century and a convenient starting point for a study of economic growth in the United Kingdom."[85] They also permit comparison of late seventeenth-century England with the England of a later day and with present-day underdeveloped countries.[86]

Although pamphleteers utilized income and expenditure estimates to support arguments, often drawing on the writings of Petty or Davenant, and although various statistical accounts were published, it was not until 1779 that England's income was again estimated, this time by Arthur Young for the year 1770. In the century that followed, eighteen annual estimates were made, and in the second quarter of the twentieth century, estimates began to be made every year.[87] Political arithmeticians in countries other than England, though they did much with vital statistical matter, produced almost no income estimates, in part presumably because data were less accessible. In France, for which many estimates were prepared in the nineteenth century, there is nothing comparable to King's estimate for an earlier period.[88] Other countries, too, lack contemporary estimates for periods before the nineteenth century.[89]

The political arithmeticians did not contribute greatly to the study of economic causation, though they did suggest ways in which statistical information could be used and made some inferences regarding the nature and the rate of economic change. Their notions of sequence and covariation flowed from inspection of data, whether tabulated or not. The political arithmeticians made little use of organons of theory, and no use of measures of association or of graphical comparison and representation. For the initial application of the graphical method, William Playfair (1759–1823) is responsible.[90] Although Playfair got from Joseph Priestley (1733–1804) the idea of using the bar graph for purposes of comparison, he also published "many excellent examples of the line graph, circle graph, . . . and pie diagram" and used them "for the discovery and analysis of economic trends."[91] Playfair's graphs, though sometimes ingenious and as a rule aesthetically attractive, were used principally for purposes of comparison, exposition, and disclosing economic changes through time.[92] Playfair exercised little influence. Jevons was perhaps the first of the later economists to mention his works (in 1879); and the use of graphs remained rare until the second half of the nineteenth century.[93]

QUESNAY, SMITH, AND MALTHUS

Economics first assumed a relatively stable form at the hands of François Quesnay and Adam Smith,[94] founders of schools which, though dissimilar in some respects, had much in common. Alert to the supposed character of man's propensities and sensible of the climate of eighteenth-century opinion, with its view of the universe as a vast machine that gave expression to a divinely contrived and essentially harmonious Order of Nature, both Quesnay and Smith inferred, or took for granted, the existence of an economic order within the larger social or world order.[95] In the works of each, therefore, statistics played a subordinate role, serving to disclose dimensions and tendencies present in the economic order and, on occasion, to give support to theses upon which economic policy might be grounded.

Quesnay made less use of quantitative matter than did Smith, whose underlying system was less rigid and perhaps more encompassing than Quesnay's. Quesnay's use of statistical data was confined largely to three articles written for Diderot's *Encyclopédie*, several years before the appearance of the *Tableau Économique* in 1758.[96] In "Fermiers," expenses involved in using horses and oxen are compared, the state of cultivation is reviewed, and costs and returns are estimated for grain cultivation and animal husbandry.[97] In "Grains," Quesnay presents estimates of average costs and returns per *arpent* planted to grain,[98] of the aggregate value of grain production under both existing conditions of "*grande*" and "*petite culture*" and realizable conditions of "*bonne culture*," and of the increase in value of output and net return attainable through a general adoption of "*bonne culture*."[99]

Smith, although he presented little data in tabular form,[100] utilized quantitative data and statements extensively in his descriptions, in his comparisons, in his indication of dimensions, and in his discussion of gains, improvements, etc.[101] His use of quantitative data, though not absolutely essential to his arguments and policy indications, facilitated them, since he could not anticipate ready acceptance of many findings and propositions in support of which he presented empirical evidence of sorts. Only after a degree of consensus had been established respecting these findings, and then only so long as this consensus obtained, would such findings and propositions be readily accepted as descriptive of a relevant underlying reality. How to measure "real value" over time—what measures to use for shorter and for longer periods—engaged Smith's attention several times, as it was to engage the attention of leading economists ever after.[102]

Both Smith and Quesnay used models as devices expository of the workings of the economy. In Smith's work, these models usually remained implicit and essentially nonquantitative, though he occasionally introduced a somewhat quantitative model or example.[103] In Quesnay's work, as in that of his followers, use was made of an arithmetical model[104] to represent the circulation of goods, services, and money within an economy.[105] This model, which is roughly translatable into terms of a Leontief input-output table, incorporated or implied the core of physiocratic theory.[106] One of Quesnay's disciples, in 1774, wrote what may be, as Spiegel suggests, one of the two earliest examples of the use of geometry in economics, the other being Bernoulli's.[107]

Malthus is touched upon here because his work is more in the empiricist tradition of Smith than in the abstract tradition of Ricardo, though he noted the mathematical character of economics.[108] Though he made virtually no use of quantitative matter in the first edition of his *Essay on the Principle of Population* (1798), he introduced considerable statistical data into later editions, of which five appeared between 1803 and 1826. In his *Principles of Political Economy* (1820, 1836) he was much concerned with "measures of value," provided a careful account of the movement of real wages, and used quantitative illustrations in his analyses of rent and profits. In general, numerical and historical data were used by him to support his main arguments.

Schools of Economic Theory and Method

The use which pre-1914 economists made of descriptive statistical data as well as quantitative approaches generally was governed largely by the canons of method regnant in the schools to which they belonged. For what was deemed the scope of economics, together with the questions posed and the methods used to find answers, varied from school to school. Six essentially distinct schools may be identified, though there is a considerable overlap between the "mathematical" school, with its emphasis on the usefulness of mathematics, and the Austrian and neoclassical schools, with their emphasis on the scope of economics. These six include the classical, the Austrian, the neoclassical, the mathematical, the historical, and the Marxian schools. Of these schools, only the neoclassical and the mathematical effectively assimilated and made use of both mathematical and statistical methods, and then only in the final third of the nineteenth century.[109] Toward the close of the period covered in this paper, eclecticism became ascendant, and there gradually came into being a composite approach that made use of both historical methods and those associated with the Austrian and the neoclassical schools. There was considerable overlap also between the mathematical and the nonmathematical schools. Only the Marxians remained distinct, and yet even their views, as set down by the revisionists, reflected the results of statistical inquiry.

THE CLASSICAL SCHOOL

The classical school, dominant in England (where it originated) during the first two-thirds of the nineteenth century and quite influential on the Continent, made little effective use of statistical matter, but found arithmetical models well suited to exposition. Its members, particularly Ricardo and J. S. Mill, but not always Malthus, were concerned principally with long-run tendencies in the growth and distribution of income and with the maintenance of a set of institutions that would foster competition and encourage economic freedom at the international level. They did not find particularly relevant, therefore, the kind of attack made on one of the school's tenets, the so-called Malthusian principle, by those who showed, statistically or otherwise, that the production of income or of wage-goods was outstripping population.[110] They did not accommodate the classical system of analysis to the growing supply of statistical materials or modify its presuppositions significantly in the light of these materials; for they were generally in agreement regarding man's relevant behavioral tendencies, their constancy, and the inferences to be drawn therefrom.[111] This failure to accommodate is more conspicuous, however, in the methodological writings of the classicists than in their discussions of problems, because methodological accounts usually place extreme and unreal emphasis upon the role of system and order in analysis.[112] Even so, J. R. McCulloch, whose efforts significantly swelled the small stock of accessible data, modified several of his opinions (e.g., those respecting the economic effects of population growth), but not all those regarding which his statistical findings might have raised doubts.[113]

Of the members of the classical school, four—Say, Senior, J. S.

Mill, and J. E. Cairnes—concerned themselves explicitly with its methodology, which is treated only implicitly in the writings of the school's founder, Ricardo.[114] No one made much use of statistics; yet all found hypothetical models useful. Ricardo, "the true founder of abstract political economy,"[115] was deductive in his approach, reasoning from premises he believed confirmed by experience. He dealt primarily with end results and the long run. His principles and inferences were illustrated or derived with the aid of arithmetical models. "I imagined strong cases that I might shew the operation of those principles."[116] He seldom had need of statistical matter and, as a rule, would have been hard put to make use of it. Even when discussing monetary and related questions, where he included statistical matter, his mode of argument remained predominantly deductive.[117]

J. B. Say, essentially an empiricist, made little use of statistics or of arithmetical models. He characterized statistics as a "descriptive" science, similar to botany, and political economy as an "experimental" science, similar to chemistry, which connected cause and effect:

> The study of statistics may gratify curiosity, but it can never be productive of advantage when it does not indicate the origin and consequences of the facts it has collected; and by indicating their origin and consequences, it at once becomes the science of political economy.[118]

Truth did not consist in "the erudition of an almanach" or in "the crude information of an office-clerk"; it was to be deduced from a small number of "essential" facts. The resulting truth of political economy consisted in "a few fundamental principles," together with "a great number of corollaries" drawn therefrom.[119] Statistical inquiry was thus of little help because it directed attention to circumstances, too many of which were inconsequential. Nor was mathematical inquiry of much help; the data on which equations might be based were too variable, with the result that specific formulations, even though adequate at the time, did not continue to hold.[120] One might even generalize too much, as Ricardo did on occasion when he pushed "his reasonings to their remotest consequences," in the absence of knowledge about the empirical validity of his extreme inferences.[121]

Although N. W. Senior and J. S. Mill lived at a time when statistical information was disclosing an improvement in living conditions despite continuation of population growth, neither found much of a role for statistical or other forms of induction in economic analysis. Both, particularly Mill, made use of illustrative models, some quantitative in character. The collection of facts, although essential to applied economics, Senior believed, was not necessary to the "theoretic branch" of economics, this being founded on a small number of relevant facts.[122] When, later, Senior came to look upon economics as a mental science which drew its "premises principally from consciousness," he found no reason to modify his opinion regarding fact collection.[123]

Mill concluded that "the method *a priori* in political economy and in all the other branches of moral science, is the only certain or scientific mode of investigation," but added that the inductive or "*a posteriori* method" might be used to verify deductions and to minimize the uncertainty arising from the complexity of particular cases and the difficulty of taking into account all the material circumstances. The method *a priori* was particularly applicable to political economy because it was concerned with man "solely as a being who desires to possess wealth, and who is capable of judging the comparative efficacy of means for obtaining that end," and therefore made "entire abstraction of every other passion or motive" except aversion to labor and desire of present enjoyment.[124]

In concrete instances, Mill agreed, only the tendency could be indicated, since it was necessary to allow for disturbing circumstances and for the fact that national cultures varied in time and space, with the result that man's response to economic (or other relevant) stimuli might vary.[125] Statistics might serve, as could history, to discover empirical laws or functional associations; but these could not be generalized to unobserved cases until the underlying permanent and preponderating connections had been established and there were grounds for resorting to use of the *a priori* method.[126]

In his *Principles,* Mill dealt much more broadly with economic subjects than his early views on method implied. Thus he occasionally employed quantitative models; and he suggested using (but did not apply) a seasonally adjusted price index. Yet he presented little quantitative information, and he gave major attention to the long-run aspects of the questions with which he dealt.[127]

Writing at a time when mathematical and statistical methods were both receiving increasing attention, Cairnes found little use for either in economic analysis, even though he thought of economic laws in terms of tendencies when disturbing causes are absent. Mathematics was unsuited to discover "economic truths," though diagrams and formulas might be used to exhibit "economic doctrines *reached by other paths*," as also might arithmetical illustrations.[128] Political economy was not susceptible of the exactness required in the domain of science, where mathematical method was applicable.[129] Experimentation being debarred, and economic behavior being the result of various causes, economics could not be an inductive science; its main methodological resource was deduction, with the office of statistical and other data confined to checking and verifying "the accuracy of our reasoning from the fundamental assumptions of the science."[130] Statistics was related to economics as it was to every science (e.g., astronomy) that had "reached the deductive stage"; it could be used to check on the tenability of the results of "deductive ratiocination."[131] Cairnes expressed alarm, therefore, at the increasingly "statistical character" of economic discussions and at the supersession of "the canon of inductive reasoning" by the "rules of arithmetic."[132] He was loath—as was Mill, and for similar reason—to induce an empirical law from statistical observations that seemed to indicate a trend, believing that an economic tendency (law) must rest upon more permanent foundations and connections than such observations could by themselves reveal.[133] Although his views, as just summarized, illustrate, as Blaug remarks, "the methodological predilections of classical economics which barred the way to quantitative verification,"[134] Cairnes was able, on occasion, to make effective use of historical and statistical data. Illustrative of the former is *The Slave Power* (1862). Exemplary of the latter is his *Essays on the Gold Question,* in which he made some use of statistical matter to assess his theoretical expectations respecting the impact of the Californian and Australian gold discoveries upon prices.[135]

THE AUSTRIAN SCHOOL

Economic behavior, Mitchell remarked, "can be studied either from outside or from inside the human being." In the former case, statistical and historical apparatus is required; in the latter it is not, though individual behavior may be formulated in mathematical terms. The Austrian school studied man from the inside. It did not, therefore, resort to induction (as spokemen for the classical school sometimes recommended) as a means of verifying inferences. It was also distrustful of such devices as index numbers, and it gave little support to mathematical method.[136] The Austrians centered their analysis upon the utility principle, finding therein both the connection between value and scarcity and a satisfactory explanation of economic behavior. They did not neglect the factor of time, insofar as economic behavior or economizing involved planning and choosing between present and future uses of resources. But they did not concern themselves with economic development and time in the long run, as did the classical and other schools; so they had no need of time series and similar instruments. In utility, however—at least in utility as envisaged by the representative individual whose economizing behavior was the subject of analysis—they had something that might be measured cardinally.

Carl Menger founded the Austrian school, though he was not the first economist to deal with utility or to use it as a point of departure,[137] and though H. H. Gossen (1810–58) was the first, according to Stigler, to state explicitly when an individual maximizes his utility, and one of the first to consider problems relating to its measurability.[138] Menger's theory, because it rested upon individual behavioral tendencies arrived at introspectively, entailed no use of statistics. Yet, because utility had or might be assigned dimensions—illustrated only arithmetically by Menger—and because Menger's theory involved ordering goods, imputation, allocating and optimizing the use of resources, and (hence) planning, his work eventuated in various arithmetical and simple algebraic models of the sort present in works of the Austrians.[139] Menger did not, however, deal with the measurability of utility or with "the value of mathematics as a tool of economic analysis."[140] In his methodological writings he emphasized the importance of theoretical economics, which was based upon deductive, atomistic analysis and which yielded universally valid laws. He distinguished theoretical economics, which dealt with general phenomena, from applied economics (e.g., policy, finance) and from economic history and statistics, which treated unique phenomena from particular points of view and which could yield restricted empirical generalizations. His own interests always lay in the field of theoretical economics.[141]

Menger's followers made no substantial changes in the role allotted to quantitative method.[142] Illustrative are the works of Menger's two best-known students, E. Böhm-Bawerk and F. von Wieser. The former describes his mode of statement, in his major work, as "abstract," but declares his theory to rest on "true empirical principles." These are obtainable from "economic history," from "statistics," and through "simple informal observation." In the study of interest and capital, however, reliance must be placed principally upon "personal observation of life." Most of the required information escapes the nets of history and statistics, partly because of its nature and partly because history and statistics necessarily gather only the "larger" facts and tend to miss many of the "more essential features of economic life." Considerable hypothetical tabular and other arithmetical matter is used, however, to expound his theories.[143]

Von Wieser, finding in "value" the "essence of things in economics," concerned himself with relevant acts and motives, with the "empirical existence of the alleged facts," and with the connection of value with other economic phenomena. The contribution that numbers or mathematics could make was essentially limited, therefore, to expressing laws governing "amounts of value"; they could not discover and trace the ramifications of "value."[144] He made use of arithmetical illustrations, however, and employed a simple simultaneous equation to explain the imputation process.[145] In his main later work he continued to rely principally upon experience derived through introspection, and to work with the assumption of a "model man" who "has never existed, nor can ever exist." The role of history and statistics, as suppliers of required empirical data, could not, therefore, be great.[146]

THE NEOCLASSICAL SCHOOL

It was principally through the activities of members of the neoclassical school and of the mathematical school[147] that quantitative method, both mathematical and statistical, came to occupy an important place in economic analysis, in part, perhaps, because of the increasing acceptance in the late nineteenth century of a statistical view of nature.[148] The neoclassical approach is most effectively represented in the works of Alfred Marshall. I am, however, also treating here the methodological critique of J. N. Keynes and the views of the mathematical economist, Edgeworth, editor of the *Economic Journal* during the ascendancy of the views of Marshall and of those (e.g., J. S. Nicholson, H. Sidgwick, P. Leroy-Beaulieu) who did not differ markedly from him. Consideration might also be given here to the work of F. W. Taussig and his students (e.g., J. Viner, F. D. Graham, J. H. Williams), all of whom undertook to test statistically the validity of the neoclassical theory of international trade.[149]

Marshall's work greatly stimulated quantification. His conception of economics as both an inductive and a deductive science, as one calling for both the collection and arrangement of facts and the analysis of interrelations among facts and their component parts (if isolable), led him to set great store by economic history, to appreciate the contributions of statistics, to make use of mathematics in analysis and in conjunction with the employment of abstract reasoning, and to focus attention upon the measurable.[150] Marshall recognized the need for both inductive and analytical studies, each being complementary to the other, particularly when the organon of economic theory was allowed a part in inductive study.[151] He found, in the complexity and in the mutability of economic matter, both limitations upon the applicability of long chains of deductive reasoning and grounds for rejecting the view that economics might approximate a physical science. In the implications of assembled historical and current data, he saw a solvent of dogma.[152]

Marshall made considerable use of graphs and included a most valuable mathematical appendix in his *Principles*, for he found in mathematics a "terse and exact language," an instrument admirably adapted to represent incremental change and "the mutual interaction of economic changes," and an undergirding for the statistical analysis of economic data.[153] Yet he remarked the limited applicability as well as the importance of mathematics (especially calculus) to economic analysis.[154] Besides his direct contribution to statistical method,[155] he developed or assessed the chain and other types of index number and proposed several methods (tabular standard, symmetallism) whereby price-level fluctuations might be countered.[156]

Both J. N. Keynes and Edgeworth dealt more extensively with the role of quantitative method in economics than did Marshall. Keynes, writing in and after 1890, at a time when the conflict between the English classical school and the German historical school was becoming less acute, declared that "according to the special department or aspect of the science under investigation, the appropriate method may be either abstract or realistic, deductive or inductive, mathematical or statistical, hypothetical or historical."[157] Political economy, though "sometimes concerned with physical laws as premises," dealt with "phenomena arising out of the economic activities of mankind in society"; it yielded both conditional conclusions and universal principles.[158] Although arithmetical examples were not suited to yield conclusions, symbolical and diagrammatic methods made for precision of statement and care in reasoning; this was of importance since political economy involved "conceptions of a mathematical nature requiring to be analysed in a mathematical spirit."[159] "The functions of statistics in economic theory are, first, to suggest empirical laws, which may or may not be capable of subsequent deductive explanation; and, secondly, to supplement deductive reasoning by checking its results, and submitting them to the test of experience."[160] In the field of applied economics, statistics, when assisted by economic theory, was more useful than in theoretical economics, facilitating "the elucidation and interpretation of particular concrete phenomena."[161] It was necessary, however, to make certain that data were sufficiently representative and reliable and that appropriate analytical techniques were used.[162] Presumably, statistics might be of use to historical economists in search of laws of economic development.[163]

Edgeworth's contribution to the introduction of mathematical method into economics, reflective always of a highly abstract bent of mind, was very great. Some of his contributions to statistical theory and practice have already been mentioned, he having contributed far more in this regard than any other economist.[164] In his statistical papers as well as in some of his economic writings, he built his argument upon probability. He was concerned, in his statistical work, "to develop the conceptions underlying the law of error, always with the idea of finding how far there was a universal law, resulting from a complex of causes, whose action could be traced in objective statistics."[165] Since the "function of the Calculus of Probabilities" was to eliminate chance, it presented the statistician with "an unattainable ideal" and thus resembled "that which the mathematical theory of Political Economy performs,"[166] a function that he described as the supply of " 'appropriate and clear' conceptions" (e.g., equilibrium, interdependence).[167] The Calculus of Probabilities—that is, a priori or "unverified" probability—also had wide application in political economy; it lent to economics "certain premises which are evidenced, neither by pure intuition, nor by formal induction, but by general impressions, and what may be called mathematical common sense."[168]

Although Edgeworth was impressed with the usefulness of the "mathematical theory of political economy" and once referred to the "empirical school" of economists as "flourishing in a chaos congenial to their mentality,"[169] he recognized the limitations of the mathematical method and the usefulness of complementary methods. Economists exaggerated the credibility of their statements based upon the postulate of perfect competition just as statisticians exaggerated the credibility of statements based upon the postulate of "complete independence of events."[170] Mathematics, though very useful, was not "an indispensable adjunct to economic studies," nor could it be used directly in any large measure in "the region of concrete phenomena."[171] Edgeworth appreciated the importance of empirical studies, and he described as very important the historical method of directly observing and generalizing from past and present facts.[172] Edgeworth's tolerant and catholic approach, together with the fact that he served as a bridge between England and the Continent, contributed greatly to the increased popularity of quantitative methods in political economy from 1890 to 1920.

The neoclassical economists objected, much as had the classical economists, to the use of quantitative methods without the guidance afforded by economic theory. This unguided use was often endorsed, explicitly or implicitly, in papers appearing in the *Journal of the Royal Statistical Society* until late in the nineteenth century.[173] With the subsequent development of advanced methods, economists sometimes failed to consider the implications of their statistical findings. Thus, H. L. Moore's statistical derivation of an upward-sloping demand curve for producers' goods prompted P. G. Wright to remark that "the need of checking statistical inductions by abstract reasoning is quite as great as that of verifying inductions by abstract statistics."[174] Similarly, A. Young, also in the neoclassical tradition, objected to F. C. Mills's argument that the economist's rational (mechanical) statement of an economic tendency was merely a statement of empirical fact or of an inductively arrived-at equation.[175]

THE MATHEMATICAL SCHOOL

The use of mathematical methods in economic analysis was still neglected in the 1860's, when Jevons' first paper advocating this method went unappreciated.[176] Yet, even before the appearance in 1838 of Cournot's path-breaking work (which went almost unnoticed for nearly forty years), about 40 mathematico-economic items had been published. Calculus had been used at least four times; analytic functions had been used several times; geometry had been employed on at least three occasions; Isnard had attempted to define a closed economic system in general equilibrium terms; Canard had expressed price determination in terms of the equilibrium of forces; Whewell had defined elasticity of demand in terms of "flexibility of price"; J. Lang had developed a macroeconomic mathematical model; tax incidence and war finance had been treated mathematically; and equations of exchange had been set down.[177] By the time Jevons' *Theory* (so stimulative of interest in mathematical method) appeared in 1871, another 60 mathematico-economic items (by thirty-one authors not included earlier) had been published, among them the second half of Von Thünen's great work, Dupuit's notable contributions, Gossen's neglected work, and significant works by C. Ellet, D. Lardner, and F. Jenkin. That interest in mathematico-economic analysis greatly increased thereafter is suggested by the fact that 106 items are reported for the period 1871–1888. A year later appeared the famous work by Auspitz and Lieben, and in 1890 the first edition of Marshall's very influential *Principles,* in which indebtedness is expressed to Cournot and Von Thünen, the contributions of other mathematical writers (e.g., Bernoulli, Jevons) are noticed, and considerable use is made of geometry and calculus. Even so, although the users of mathematical method gradually increased in number, the method did not really come into its own until after World War I.

Although the adoption of mathematical method was influenced by various circumstances (among them the state of economic theory, the issues considered important, the economic knowledge of mathematicians, and the mathematical equipment of students who became interested in economics), a certain amount of order underlies its adoption. It appears to be true, at least after there has been some quantification, that, as Stigler finds, more general formulations tend to replace less general ones, and more manageable formulations tend to be preferred to those less manageable; it may also be true, if economists are of an empirical turn of mind, that theories not congruent with reality tend to be given up.[178] The introduction and adoption of a mathematical approach were relatively likely in the past only when an economically relevant phenomenon was considered measurable and there existed strong motives for measuring it; it was retarded by the persistence of emphasis upon description.

The economic phenomena that came to be recognized as being measurable, either hypothetically or empirically, and that therefore might be dealt with in terms of symbols, indices, curves, or equations, were of various sorts. They may be grouped under six headings: (1) response of prices to changes in the quantity of money; (2) response of "utility" to changes in the quantity of utility-producing means at an individual's disposal; (3) response of purchases and (later) supplies to price or income changes; (4) response of entrepreneurial profit, to changes in volume of goods sold or in quantity of factors hired; (5) conditions of general equilibrium, together with the process of equilibration; (6) special phenomena, whose study resulted in a merger of mathematical and statistical methods. Of these groups, (1) and (2) were the first to command considerable and growing interest; then (3) and (4);

then (5) and (6), provided that tax incidence is included under (3) or (4).

1. Although the response of prices to changes in the quantity of money was the first economic phenomenon whose quantitative character was recognized (it having been noted by Bodin in 1568 and quite possibly by earlier observers), the relation between prices and money was not expressed in crude algebraic terms until the late seventeenth century, and not at all correctly until the early nineteenth century. Thereafter, the quantity equation gradually came into wider use, but it was increasingly employed with awareness of its limitations, and sometimes it was elaborated. In the first crude algebraically expressed equations of exchange, J. Briscoe's of 1694 and H. Lloyd's of 1771, the role and variability of velocity were ignored, and they continued to be ignored by Lloyd's Italian contemporaries, who sometimes combined a Say type of demand-supply price function with the equation of exchange.[179] Not until the early nineteenth century, long after literary economists had stressed its importance, was a velocity coefficient introduced into the equation of exchange, by J. Lang in 1811, by L. de S. Cagnazzi in 1813, and by S. Turner in 1819.[180] Roscher used an equation quite like Turner's as early as 1854; F. Bowen, one like Cagnazzi's in 1856; and Levasseur, in 1858, and S. Newcomb, in 1886, a Fisherine sort of equation, this type having been stated by J. W. Lubbock in 1840 and by K. H. Rau in 1841.[181] During the last quarter of the nineteenth century and the early part of the twentieth, economists continued to differ somewhat concerning the precise nature of the relationship between money and prices; yet nearly all of them employed a quantity-type of equation.[182]

2. Both the rise and the decline in importance of utility theory were dominated by mathematical economists, several of whom (Cournot, Cassel, and Moore) found it of no use in economic analysis, even though, until the 1920's or after, the majority of economists considered it helpful. Bernoulli, in 1738, discussed utility with the aid of calculus, as did two of its three popularizers (Jevons and Walras, but not Menger) in the 1870's and several of its leading critics in the early twentieth century. Of the many writers who supposed that "equal increments of utility-producing means . . . yield diminishing increments of utility," some were content with

verbal or arithmetical statements (e.g., Buffon, Bentham, Menger), whereas others (e.g., Dupuit, Gossen, Jevons, Walras) represented the utility function in geometrical or other mathematical terms, and Bernoulli even postulated its precise shape. This postulate commanded supporters again between 1860 and 1914, on grounds of analytical convenience and the supposed relevance of the Weber-Fechner "law," and despite the untenability of the view that there existed a generally suitable function of some particular shape.[183]

The popularity of utility theory was largely attributable to the uses to which the theory could supposedly be put: for example, to explain how exchange benefited exchangers; to systematize price theory and account for factor prices in terms of derived demand; to account for downward-sloping demand curves; to establish the theorem of maximum satisfaction and the possibility of multiple equilibria; to reveal, at the individual level, conditions for maximizing utility and for equilibrating the exchange of labor for goods; to afford solutions to problems to which the concept of consumer's surplus was supposedly adapted; and to undergird "welfare"-maximizing policies or aspirations. In the end, however, economists found this popularity misplaced and utility less useful than had been supposed. The mathematical economists contributed to this outcome when, after having clarified the meaning of a utility function and its relation of demand, they discovered, first, various difficulties relating to the measurability of utility and its application to the assessment of policy, and then that the economists could get along without measurable utility and make do with ordinal indices, etc.[184]

No quantitative concept occupied a more prominent place in the literature than that of the graphically represented notion of consumer's surplus, sometimes expressed in terms of utility and sometimes in terms of the difference between what consumers paid and what they would have been willing to pay. Use of the concept thus presupposed use of a demand curve or of some sort of utility curve to represent the aggregate of "cost" and "surplus." This quantitative notion of a surplus (perhaps rejected by Cournot) was first discovered and propounded in 1844 by a French bridge engineer and elaborated forty-five years later by Auspitz and Lieben in their remarkable book (1889) on the behavior of consumers and firms; it was arrived at independently by the English engineer, Fleeming

Jenkin (1871), and by A. Marshall (1890),[185] who first called it "consumer's surplus" and, through his treatment of it, gave rise to much of the discussion that took place during the ensuing half century. Dupuit was interested in determining the extent to which public works are justified and how their services should be priced. He discovered how public and private monopolies should price, the uses of discriminatory pricing, and a theoretical justification for a general sales tax. Jenkin employed the concept (together with that of producer's surplus) to show the advantages of trade as well as the disadvantage of a commodity tax, which, he maintained, injured the taxpayers more than it benefited the state.[186] Marshall directed his discussion of the concept more to the assessment of policy possibilities than did Auspitz and Lieben, who were particularly concerned with developing theoretical propositions and their implications.[187] Despite the criticisms to which the concepts of utility and consumer's surplus were subjected, the latter continued in use until the 1930's.

3. Cournot was the first to make both demand and supply functions of price (so that $D = f(P)$ and $S = f(P)$, where D stands for demand, S for supply, and P for price), just as Wicksteed was the first (1910) to attempt to combine the two curves.[188] Cournot did not derive his demand function from a utility function. Instead, he considered the probable properties of a collective demand function, how they might vary with type of market, how what we call elasticity might vary, etc., and he noted that in his day it was not yet possible to arrive at an "empiric formula." He did not say much about the supply function.[189]

The demand function was present in Dupuit's work. Jenkin used supply and demand functions, as did Jevons, in his teaching, if not so unambiguously in his *Theory*. Von Mangoldt included both functions in his *Grundriss* (1863), as did W. Launhardt (follower of Walras and Jevons) in his *Mathematische Begründung* (1885).[190] So did Auspitz and Lieben and Marshall, whose work popularized the use of industrial supply and demand curves. The concept of price elasticity, long virtually restricted to demand curves, was implicit in works of Cournot and others, but it did not become popular until Marshall made it explicit and geometrical (1885, 1890).[191] That a decrease in the price of a consumer's commodity might sometimes be accompanied by a decrease in its consumption, a possibility noted in the course of the controversy over utility, had been remarked by Dupuit, Auspitz and Lieben, and Marshall.[192]

Utilizers of the Cournot type of demand function usually supposed that prices other than that of the commodity under consideration remained virtually constant, as did also tastes and income. Walras departed from this practice when he enunciated the law of demand of the Lausanne school in 1873, making demand for a given commodity depend upon the prices of all commodities; his statement of supply was correspondingly complex.[193] In time, demand was made to depend also on income and its distribution, together with other relevant factors.[194]

If exception is made of Gregory King's "Law" (discussed by Pareto and many others and noted in Section III) and of somewhat similar formulations by E. Engel (1861), the able statistician E. Laspeyres (1875), and Farquhar (1891),[195] it may be said that not until after the turn of the century was it recognized that economic functions, since they are potentially empirical as well as theoretical, might be estimated by fitting curves to properly manipulated data.[196] Thus Benini (1907), Gini (1910), Pigou (1910), a very able M. Lenoir (1913), R. Lehfeld (1914), and H. L. Moore (1914, 1917) variously fitted such curves. After the war, such curve-fitting was intensified.[197]

The growth of interest in the statistical character of demand functions was paralleled by that of interest in Engel's law, first formulated in 1857, on the basis of data whose collection had been stimulated by the unrest of the 1840's. The purpose of the law was to describe how expenditure upon particular categories of goods responded to increases in income. It might have given rise to general and comparative studies, like that of Houthakker cited below; but this did not happen. A number of studies were made, however, though without significant results, by Engel, by C. D. Wright (1875), by Schwabe (1868), by Laspeyres (1875), and later by Del Vecchio (1912) and Ogburn (1916).[198] Although additional studies are cited by C. C. Zimmerman, it was not until the 1930's and the appearance of Allen and Bowley's *Family Expenditure* (1935), with its linear curves, that expenditure-pattern study really began to flourish[199] and economists began to interest themselves seriously in income effects and elasticities. Stigler attributes the delay to (*a*) the long-held supposition that income changes very slowly and hence may be treated as almost invariable, and (*b*) the belief that income was not an important variable in many of the problems of concern to economists.[200]

4. Given independent functions of demand and supply, it was inevitable that partial equilibria would become the subject of study of mathematical economists, particularly since the concept of mechanical equilibrium had long been an integral part of European natural philosophy. The partial equilibria assumed two forms: (*a*) industrial, when conditions of competition (first defined with precision by Cournot)[201] obtained; and (*b*) firm, when conditions of imperfect competition prevailed.[202] Cournot, Jevons, Jenkin, Von Mangoldt, Auspitz and Lieben, and Marshall contributed importantly to the analysis of equilibrium within particular competitive industries. This was the type of equilibrium most commonly considered from the 1870's or 1880's on until the 1920's, when growth of interest in imperfect competition and the use of the firm as a point of departure caused firm equilibrium to become ascendant and once again focused attention on decision-makers and decision-making. Since it has been noted that the use of geometry in theoretic economics had greatly increased in the late nineteenth and early twentieth centuries, it may also be noted that the inferiority of geometry to symbols was also beginning to be recognized.[203]

Although Cournot and Von Thünen are describable as the initiators of the study of firm equilibrium, this study was anticipated by Buquoy, who in 1815 indicated that a firm's profit maximum with respect to the use of a service was at the point where marginal net return over cost is zero.[204] Cournot, starting with a monopolist confronted by a collective demand curve, derived a marginal revenue curve from the latter and showed that the monopolist's profit maximum would be at the point where his marginal revenue and his marginal cost coincided. Then, on the basis of assumptions regarding the conjecture of each seller respecting what other sellers would do, Cournot extended his analysis to situations in which there were two, three, or more sellers, adding that when sellers had become sufficiently numerous each would disregard the others and "unlimited competition" would prevail. He was able, in the light of this analysis, to describe tax incidence under various conditions and to show that price is lower when a composite commodity is made by one rather than by separate monopolists, each responsible for a segment.[205]

Von Thünen, in contrast with Cournot, focused attention, in 1850, on the behavior of individual agricultural operators (functioning much as hired managers) in an isolated-state model and developed a mathematical theory of wage and interest-rate determination. His theory, in essence, was a marginal productivity theory—according to which "the general level of wages in the state is determined by the increment in product value produced by the last added worker," with employers standing ready to hire workers up to the point where this increment and the wage paid coincided—and it became the basis for later nineteenth-century marginal productivity theories.[206] This study, together with contributions of the Austrian and the Lausanne schools, paved the way for the development of statistical production functions, of which the most popular have been the Cobb-Douglas type, first developed in the 1920's.[207] Similarly, Von Thünen's work must eventually have set in motion the line of inquiry which resulted in the application of Euler's theorem to the analysis of functional distribution, first by P. H. Wicksteed (1894), and subsequently by others interested in whether competitive distribution exhausted the product.[208]

In the closing third of the century, it came to be accepted that the price an entrepreneur stood ready to pay for the services of any factor would not exceed the estimated marginal value of these services to this entrepreneur. Accordingly, it was the selling behavior of the entrepreneur, rather than his hiring behavior, that commanded most attention and gave rise to controversy. Mathematical economists remarked that, under conditions of imperfect competition, the equilibrium price would be different than under conditions of perfect competition;[209] and they agreed respecting the outcome of monopoly pricing. They differed somewhat concerning price and stability under conditions of duopoly and bilateral monopoly; and it came to be recognized that an author's assumptions fixed his conclusion. Oddly enough, except for an occasional recognition of a monopsonistic situation (e.g., by Wicksteed), or of the possible influence of trade unionism, the impact of imperfect competition upon factor pricing was not explored. It was commonly supposed that monopsony did not exist or that the services of factors were forthcoming to entrepreneurs under conditions of highly elastic supply.[210] It was not until after World War I, therefore, that mathematical economists concerned themselves with the territory lying between the realm of competition and that of monopoly.

5. There is not much to be said about the general equilibrium systems. Such a system was suggested and partly described by Isnard (1781); its existence was recognized in part by Cournot (1838) and may have been implied by Jevons (1871). It was first given full expression by Walras (1874), popularized by Cassel after 1900, and dealt with by Marshall and Pareto, among others. The development of such a system presupposed a minimal knowledge of mathematics and an understanding of the economy as a system of prices. It could not have begun to be significantly appreciated until the second half of the nineteenth century, given the then prevailing knowledge of mathematics and the pricing mechanism. But when it did begin to be appreciated, the days of residual theories, simple marginal productivity systems, and simple functions became numbered.[211]

6. In the foregoing account, no detailed attention was given to K. Wicksell, who, along with G. Cassel, played a major part in introducing mathematical economics into Sweden; nor to V. Pareto, who, together with his students, introduced mathematical method into the *Giornale degli Economisti,* and who, as successor to Walras, helped to popularize this method on the Continent and foresaw that the progress of economic science would depend largely upon "the investigation of empirical laws that are derived from statistics";[212] nor to the whole of the work of Auspitz and Lieben; nor to that of I. Fisher and H. L. Moore, who, along with W. M. Persons, played the major role in quantifying American economics; nor to the increasing use of geometrical models in and after the 1890's (e.g., Cunynghame's), despite their being unsuited to represent situations involving more than two, and certainly more than three, interdependent variables. More important in its ultimate impact than the work of any one of the authors just listed is the process whereby statistical and mathematico-economic analysis merged. To this process many contributed: Edgeworth by his theoretical work,

Bowley, Hooker, Lehfeld, Cassel, Pareto and his school, I. Fisher and W. M. Persons, and others.

The change that took place between 1860–1880 and 1900–1917 with respect to this merging process may be illustrated by a detailed comparison of the work of Jevons, much of which has already been referred to, and that of H. L. Moore, a number of whose major contributions came after 1917.[213] Writing at a time when uniform geometrical growth rates were often postulated, Jevons was content to use such a rate in his estimation (in *The Coal Question,* 1865) of future coal requirements; Moore would probably have fitted a trend, taking into account obstacles. Jevons' use of forecasting diagrams, though somewhat reminiscent of Playfair, was original, as was much of his use of graphs. His approach to fluctuations in time, that of a meteorologist, enabled him to isolate seasonal variation and secular movement and to set cycles apart; it compelled him to develop suitable index numbers and prompted him to inquire into the impact of price inflation (arising from the gold discoveries) on incomes, budgets, national debt, etc. His further study of prices and of index numbers, together with his inference from T. Rogers' study of prices, led him to conclude that the solar cycle (as then measured) and the trade cycle (as he measured it) were associated as cause and effect, though he never completely settled on the nature of the nexus. In his *Theory* (1871), "the first treatise to present in a finished form the theory of value based on subjective valuations,"[214] algebra and diagrams are employed to describe the working of the marginal principle, and statistical demand curves are foreshadowed, as perhaps are job analysis and time-and-motion study.[215]

Moore began to write after some of the shortcomings of utility theory (which he found unnecessary to economic analysis) had been discovered; after Edgeworth and Pearson and others had established modern statistical method; after Walras' price theory had become a part of economic theory; and after Pareto had begun to combine mathematical and statistical methods. Moore integrated the newer statistical and economic theory, with emphasis upon induction, but not to the exclusion of the a priori. The first fruits of this merged approach were assembled in his *Laws of Wages* (1911), in which, with distributive theory in mind, he obtained measures or strong indications of the impact of a number of factors (e.g., cost of the standard of life, average productivity, the distribution of ability, trade unionism and strikes, age of worker, size of establishment, etc.) upon the structure and the movement of wages, particularly in France, for which a large amount of statistical information had been compiled. Subsequently, he measured trade-cycle changes, making use of periodigram analysis, sought to account for them in exogenous terms (as had Jevons), and finally established the methods on which statistical price analysis was based in the United States in the early 1930's.[216]

THE HISTORICAL SCHOOL

In the historical school I include the leading earlier and later German economists who emphasized the superiority of historical over other methods of economic analysis, together with those English, continental, and (later) American economists who came to share the German historical economists' unfavorable opinion of the abstract, deductive approaches of the classical and the Austrian economists. This unfavorable opinion was, more than anything else, the single element common to all members of the school; and even respecting it they differed, since some (e.g., Roscher) were much less critical than others (e.g., Knies, Hildebrand, List) of the classical school, and still others (e.g., Schmoller) eventually became appreciative of the methods of nonhistorical economists.[217]

Such unity of approach as the German historical economists derived from their opposition to the abstract, deductive approach of the English classical school had its origin in a number of circumstances. Prominent among these were the imperfect adaptation to the solution of German problems (e.g., industrial development, transportation, agriculture) of principles compatible with current English experience, as well as the degree to which historical or evolutionist methods and concepts were used by early nineteenth-century German students of jurisprudence, politics, philology, and philosophy. Non-German members of the historical school, though largely inspired by German exemplars, were influenced also by evolutionist opinions of the sort which flourished already in the late eighteenth century.[218]

The members of the historical school found mathematics inapplicable to the study of society, even as had A. Comte, an advocate of the exclusive use of historical method and (like Hegel) a proponent of the view that humanity developed "according to recognizable laws."[219] In essence, the historical economists believed that models amenable to mathematical formulation were too simple to represent complex social relationships. But they did believe, as in part did ordinary economic historians, that statistics were of great use in facilitating the discovery of laws of economic development, the study of concrete questions, and the application of economics to the solution of problems.[220] They seem not to have been unduly concerned by the fact that history deals with unique events or that there existed too few collectives (e.g., nations) to constitute a universe of units amenable to statistical analysis. Instead they found, in the assembly and study of statistical data relating to a particular event or collective, a means of obtaining a better understanding of this object, as well as the ability to compare it with other objects. Furthermore, because they assigned to the state a large economic role that could not be carried out without a great deal of statistical information, they found themselves compelled to emphasize the importance of quantitative investigation, and several (e.g., B. Hildebrand, K. T. von Inama-Sternegg) became heads of statistical bureaus.

Considerable use was made of statistics by both the German and the non-German members of the historical school, but not of advanced techniques, most of which came into use only during the school's decline. Levasseur and W. J. Ashley made extensive use of quantitative matter, the latter even employing it to support protectionism.[221] Hildebrand, having become director of the Thüringian statistical bureau in 1864, published many statistical studies in this capacity, as well as in his capacity as editor of the *Jahrbücher für Nationalökonomie und Statistik.* Earlier, he had made some use of statistics in a critique of F. Engels' work.[222] Knies merely touched upon statistics in his prolegomena to the historical school, having sharply distinguished between history and statistics in his 1850 work.[223] W. Roscher was aware of the advantages of the mathematical mode of analysis, but believed economic life too complicated to permit effective use of algebraic formulas. Statistical methods, however, he found similar to the historical method in applicability.[224] Roscher had in mind primarily conclusion-suggesting comparisons of magnitudes. Schmoller, by contrast, thought of statistics as a method of systematic mass observation, together with classification and comparison in space and time. Statistics could then substitute for experiment and facilitate the scaling of functional causes, and it could suggest hypotheses. But it could not disclose the underlying nature of things or the complex of causes at work.[225] Because he was the leading spokesman for the so-called later historical school, Schmoller was able to give strong support to quantitative inquiry of the simpler sort that was in vogue in the second half of the nineteenth century. He provided an outlet for such inquiries in his *Jahrbuch für Gesetzgebung, Verwaltung, und Volkswirtschaft,* and he himself undertook some statistical investigations, among them studies of long-run wage changes and of the stability of income distribution.[226] The latter work of the historical school did not reflect the revolution in statistical method that got under way in the 1890's or the growing interest in mathematical methods.[227]

THE MARXIST SCHOOL

Several kinds of quantitative data abound in Marx's *Capital.* First, many arithmetical models and illustrations are employed to expound his organon, to reveal the laws of motion operative in capitalistic societies, and to disclose the anticipated eventual collapse of the capitalistic economy. Second, statistical matter is used to lend support to his conclusions about the behavior and the unsanguine prospects of capitalism and to persuade the reader of the validity of these conclusions.[228] Marx's conclusions are not statistically induced; they follow, supposedly, from the premises or principles present, in his opinion, in the capitalistic system. His underlying method thus resembled, in its deductive aspects, that of Ricardo, by whom Marx was much influenced.

Two sorts of quantitative problems troubled pre-1914 Marxians. The first arose from Marx's inability to transform values completely into prices and his consequent resort to an illogical method. Since then, however, supposedly satisfactory solutions based upon simultaneous equations have been forthcoming, some in the past decade.[229] The second arose out of the course taken by real wages, especially in Germany. Marx had supposed that, as capitalism moved from crisis to crisis to its final collapse, real wages would fall and the misery of the working class would inevitably increase, a supposition still repeated in Moscow.[230] It was evident by the close of the century, however, that misery was not increasing, that real wages had risen. Whence "Marxist" E. Bernstein called for a revision of socialist theory and strategy.[231] The revisionist proposals were rejected, however, by the orthodox socialists (especially K. Kautsky), who contended that, even though real wages had risen, misery had increased, since income inequality was increasing.[232] The problem then became one of showing that inequality was increasing, a conclusion the orthodox Marxists had difficulty supporting. Out of this situation, however, came the stimulus for studying income distribution around 1900.

Lenin, unlike the more scholarly Marx, conceived of statistical data as strategic and tactical instruments. They might serve to disclose the nature and the rate of socioeconomic change and to furnish bases for propaganda. His use of data, even when straightforward,[233] was unimpressive and inferior to Marx's. In sum, while the Marxists did not retard the adoption of quantitative method by economists, they did not accelerate its introduction except insofar as Kautsky's attack on revisionist Marxism prompted bourgeois economists to study income distribution.

Periodical Literature

The impression one gets from the preceding review is reducible to several inferences. First, mathematical economics made little headway before the 1870's. Cournot's work was hardly known before that time. The influence of Von Thünen, though greater and though felt in France and Germany, still was limited. Second, even though the mathematical method commanded increasing attention from 1870 to 1910, the number of authors who used it was very small, and the works employing this method were the product of this small number. Third, until the closing third of the century, there was little progress in statistical method. There was, of course, a large and growing body of statistical data, especially in tabular form, but these data were interpreted largely through inspection; there was little or no use of measures of dispersion. Even the use of index numbers was limited. Fourth, the final third of the century witnessed, first, attempts to remove seasonal variation, to decompose time series into cyclical and secular movements, and then attempts to compare deviations from trends. In the closing years of the century this sort of analysis was facilitated by the newly discovered instrument of correlation, an instrument that came to be employed to discover associations between time series and to separate noncausal from seemingly causal factors. Fifth, the great change in statistical methods and procedures took place during and immediately after the 1890's. Sixth, with the development of these procedures and the parallel development of mathematically expressed economic theory came recognition that a merger of these two approaches would make economics a science that was empirical and inductive as well as theoretical and a priori.

What has been said is borne out by analysis of the content of the economic and statistical periodicals which began publication in the nineteenth century and which continued throughout the period under survey. Several date from around 1840, several from the 1850's and 1860's, one from the 1870's, and a number from the 1880's and 1890's. Of the early statistical journals, we may consider the *Journal of the Royal Statistical Society*, which began in 1837, twenty-three years before the *Journal de la société de statistique de Paris*. During the first fifty years of its existence, there appeared in the *JRSS* many articles on commercial, industrial, and financial statistics and subjects (with much relevant statistical matter and interpretation supplied). Nearly three tenths of the titles related to such materials, whereas only just over four tenths dealt with moral, social, and vital-statistical matter.[234] This journal, as well as other journals, performed in some measure a role performed today by government documents. Among the many subjects dealt with in the *JRSS* (in articles often long, usually rich in tabular materials, and sometimes adorned with graphs),[235] one finds prices and wages and changes therein; progress of the working class; decline in pauperism; trade-cycle and related phenomena; debt and taxes; income distribution and changes, usually inferred from tax returns; banking and clearing-house data; foreign trade, trends and international differences therein; gold movements and exchange rates; international differences in wealth and economic progress; agriculture, land use, and the impact on the Old World of progress in cereal cultivation in the New World; the economic bases of national strength and Britain's long-run economic and commercial prospects; the future of India and the United States; the economic impact of war; the advantages to be had from colonies; the role and formation of human capital; the future of the coal supply, together with its significance; the superiority of British to non-British workmen and its significance for protectionism; rail transportation and its effects; capital accumulation.

The papers in the *JRSS* were descriptive and analytical either in the manner of the classical school or, more frequently, in that of statistical-inductive students who had little use for explicit, deductive theory; the statistical indicators were simple, yet the analysis was often of a high order, and much information was presented that was of use to economists and policy-makers and that stimulated further inquiry. Representative are the many papers contributed by C. Babbage, R. D. Baxter, E. Chadwick, P. G. Craigie, W. Farr, R. Giffen, W. A. Guy, L. Levi, W. Newmarch, and R. H. I. Palgrave. Neither in these papers, nor in the occasional discussions of the role of statistics in economic research, was account taken of methods which, though applicable in or after the 1840's, were not utilized until in and after the 1880's, under the leadership of Edgeworth, Yule, and Pearson.[236] After the 1880's (which saw publication of papers by Edgeworth, Poynting, and Marshall), articles dealing with advanced statistical theory, or involving the use of new or improved measures of economic distribution and change (e.g., measures of correlation and association and of central tendency and dispersion, curves such as Pareto's, index numbers), became increasingly frequent; old-fashioned articles, now confined largely to noneconomic topics, diminished in number.[237]

Even after the composition of the *JRSS* began to change markedly in and after the 1890's, the older tradition persisted in the *Bulletin de l'institut international de statistique,* which reflected the interests of its heterogeneous and international membership. Few of the economic papers involved the use of newer statistical or mathematical methods (though these were sometimes treated in papers appearing in the *Bulletin*). In Volumes I through VII (1886–93) there appeared papers on clearings, railways, index numbers, price and wage statistics and movements, international trade and gold and silver movements, local and progressive taxation, trade cycle and its measurement, finance and public debt, family budgets, property distribution, national wealth, savings, income distribution and material welfare (by E. Engel), and measures of the economic condition of peoples. In the next nine volumes (1895–1907) the subjects treated included prices and wages and their movements, living conditions, cost of living, international trade, the trade cycle, income distribution, the concept and measurement of national income, mobile property, savings, successions, employment, transportation, agricultural topics, balance sheets, savings institutions, fiscal charges, precious metals, occupational composition, agricultural concentration, private wealth, typology, sources of statistical regularity, and "statistical laws." In the final four prewar volumes (1908–15) there were papers on wages, prices, index numbers, gold production, balance of payments, distribution of property and income, economic forecasting, unemployment, estimating national wealth, statistical comparisons, and rendering curves comparable.[238]

The contents of the *Publications* of the American Statistical Association (predecessor of the Association's *Journal*) were somewhat more technical than those of the *Bulletin,* gradually reflecting the progress in English statistical theory after 1890, when *Publications* began. Population prediction was treated in 1891 (II, 278); averages and price-wage indices in 1893 (III, 141, 496); the neglect of statistics by American governments and colleges in 1897 (V, 180); the Lorenz curve in 1904–5 (IX, 210); price-wage indices, cumulative curves, and measures of dispersion in 1906–7 (X, 110, 319); log-log curves, supposedly indicative of increasing concentration of wealth, in 1908–9 (XI, 27); positive association of increase in use of statistics with passing of *laissez faire* in 1908–9 (XI, 431); and discussion of I. Fisher's estimate of the velocity of circulation in 1910–11 (XII, 28). Correlation was dealt with in this number (287), in 1912–13 (XIII, 174), and in 1916–17 (XV, 602, 670, 847, 854), along with the ratio chart (*ibid.,* 577, 805) and with limitations of both graphic analysis (205) and of currently used measures of wealth concentration (471). In 1914–16 (XIV 11, 612), the possible contributions of statistics to economics were discussed.

Interests on the Continent in the middle portion of the nineteenth century seem to be well represented in the *Journal des économistes* (which began in 1842), in *De Economist,* which started in 1852, and in *Jahrbücher für Nationalökonomie und Statistik.* Considerable statistical material appeared in the first and second of these journals, but little or nothing on newer statistical methods, and not much on the use of mathematical method in economics. In the *Journal,* M. Wolkoff, French translator of Von Thünen, discussed the latter's natural wage in 1856 and 1857 (X, 263; XVI, 239); Dupuit published many papers between 1849 and 1865; G. Fauveau used this method when discussing taxation in 1867–71 (V, 31; XIII, 391; XVI, 466; XXIV, 445) and freedom to work in 1885 (XXXI, 345); Walras discussed the monetary standard in 1882 (XX, 5). Still, emphasis upon refined and advanced quantitative methods was limited, in part perhaps because some relevant papers were published elsewhere.

In *De Economist,* statistics were treated in the traditional manner, much as in several Dutch journals which antedated *De Economist;* considerable data were presented, but methodology and statistical theory were neglected. Mathematical method was also neglected, though Walras' *Elements* was reviewed in 1889 by A. Beaujon, who assigned mathematics a secondary role. In 1895, C. A. Verrijn Steuart reviewed literature on index numbers, including the views of N. Pierson, who found them of little use. It was not until the present century that Dutch economists adopted advanced quantitative methods.

Much statistical matter appeared in the *Jahrbücher,* but not many mathematical or highly technical statistical discussions. Von Thünen's wage theory was treated in 1867 (IX, 425); the use of the median in 1870 (XIV, 183); the measurement of price change by E. Laspeyres in 1871 (XVI, 296) and in 1864 (III, 81) and by H. Paasche in 1878 (XXX, 165, 245). In 1878, the role of mathematical method in economics was reviewed and the *JRSS* bibliography of mathematical-economic works was reproduced (XXXI, 295, 379). In 1879, A. Soetbeer classified Prussian income receivers in several ways (XXXIV, 112). Lexis dealt with stability in 1879 (XXXII, 60);

Westergaard, with probability in 1885 (XLIV, 1) and with interpolation in 1895 (LXIV, 183); and Von Bortkiewicz with interpolation and other issues in 1894–96 (LXIII, 641; LXIV, 183; LXV, 321; LVI, 671) and with probability and small numbers in 1899 and 1910 (LXXII, 230; XCIV, 218). Gossen's work was discussed in 1910 (XL, 483), and statistical questions in 1909 and 1913 (XXXVIII, 1; XLV, 1).

Of the American economic periodicals, only *Quarterly Journal of Economics* carried a number of papers on advanced quantitative method between the late 1880's and 1917. Much tabular material, together with simple graphs and index numbers, was to be found in all the journals, however.[239] In the *Journal of Political Economy* there appeared in 1892–93 (II, 20, 68, 193, 274) statistical evidence pertaining to price interrelations, farmer discontent, and free trade and prosperity, and a diagram descriptive of compensatory bimetallism; in 1893–94 (II, 235, 517), a somewhat mathematical study of profits and an analysis of California prices; in 1894–95 (III, 145, 203), inductive studies of money and prices; in 1895–96 (IV, 515), a critique of index numbers; and in 1898–99 (VII, 42, 204), papers on measuring the value of money and making social applications of probability. Index numbers were discussed occasionally in between 1900 and 1902 (VIII, 171; X, 1–71, 193) and between 1910 and 1916 (XVIII, 294, 345, 513; XIX, 269; XXI, 500, 681, 798 ff.; XXIV, 126, 625). In the *Publications* of the American Economic Association, there appeared, besides the works of Mayo-Smith and Norton already mentioned, accounts of the study of statistics (III [1], 1888, 5; IV [5], 1889, 37; VI [1], 1891, 64); papers in which index numbers and averages were used (VIII [1], 1893, 108; XI [4], 1896, 331); and important statistical studies (e.g., V [3–4], 1904). In the *American Economic Review* there appeared in Volume I (1911), besides abstracts of mathematical and statistical literature (a department thereafter conducted by Allyn Young), papers on seasonal variation, correlation of price indices, and the equation of exchange (33, 120, 296), which was again discussed, along with price forecasts, in 1912 (II, 102, 302, 531). In Volume III (1913), index numbers (1), business forecasts (43), and the equation of exchange and price forecasts (341) were discussed; and in 1914 (IV, 793), the movement of real wages. In Volume VI (1916), the effect of property growth upon depreciation reserves was treated mathematically (69); Persons described his business barometer (739); and Fairchild discussed the standard of living (9). Railroad valuation and real wages were discussed in 1917 (VII, 31, 319). In the *Quarterly Journal*, averages were treated in 1886–87 (I, 83); Von Thünen's wage theory in 1894–95 (IX, 291, 388); Marx's *Capital* in 1895–96 (X, 1);[240] Cournot's work in 1897–98 (XII, 119, 238; also, XIX, 370); index numbers in 1907–8 (XXI, 613) and 1910–12 (XXIV, 750; XXV, 161, 613); the influence of crops on business in 1906–7 (XX, 323); the quality of statistical materials in 1912–13 (XXVI, 673). Monetary statistics and policy were discussed several times (XXVI, 1912–13, 140; XXVII, 1913–14, 213, 385, 401); and so were measures of wealth and income concentration (XXIII, 416; XXIV, 160, 180; XXV, 216; XXVIII, 255). H. L. Moore stressed the importance of inductive economics, reviewing notable contributions (e.g., those of Cournot, Jevons, Edgeworth, Bortkiewicz, Pareto, Benini, and Lexis) in "The Statistical Complement of Pure Economics"[241] (XXIII, 1908–9, 1) and emphasizing the danger of extending to unexplored reality conclusions that are founded solely on hypotheses ("Paradoxes of Competition," XX, 1905–6, 211). P. G. Wright, critic of Moore's work on cycles (XXIX, 1914–15, 631), treated the relation of the magnitude of consumer's surplus to degree of inequality of income distribution (XXXI, 1917–18, 301).

Much graphic and tabular material was included in the *Revue de économie politique* (1887 ff.), in the *Giornale degli Economisti* (1875 ff.), and in the *Economic Journal* (1890 ff.). Many mathematical articles were included in the *Giornale*, and a number[242] in the *Economic Journal* and the *Revue* (including three articles and a review by Walras, 1887, 1889, 1890, 1898, and a review by Pareto, 1902). Also worthy of note are mathematical or statistical articles in the *Revue:* 1887 (345), 1890 (16), 1893 (257), 1894 (237, 927), 1895 (201 ff.), 1896 (589 ff.), 1897 (769), 1900 (167 ff., 580), 1901 (817 ff.), 1902 (576), 1904 (477 ff., 702), 1908 (430 ff.), 1909 (532, 581), 1911 (28, 681), 1912 (452, 541, 748), 1913 (462), 1914 (401, 576), 1915 (101). The *Giornale* did not become an important repository of mathematical articles until 1891, when Pareto became a fairly regular contributor, to be followed by members of what may be called his school—for example, R. Benini in 1897 and Ricci in 1904. Occasional articles by Walras, P. des Essars, Boninsegni, Perozzo, Scorza, and others began to appear in the late 1890's. In sum, in and after the 1890's the *Giornale* carried more articles involving mathematical or advanced statistical method than did its economic contemporaries. The *Economic Journal* included, besides Edgeworth's papers and regular notes on contributions in the field of advanced quantitative method, many somewhat less technical papers. Among these fall papers on human capital (I, 1891, 105); on exchange, savings, and state-expenditure/wealth ratios (II, 1892, 35, 290, 561); on the bases of Britain's commercial supremacy and on consumer's rent (IV, 1894, 342, 456, 595, 716); on price indices (V, 1895, 329; VI, 1896, 327; VII, 1897, 247, 346); on correlation and mathematical method (V, 1895, 113, 603); and on long-run wage movements (VIII, 1898, 476; IX, 1899, 588; XI, 1901, 151). In 1903 (XIII, 303, 313), common statistical errors were described and the impact of duties was analyzed graphically. Geometrical, statistical, and algebraic analyses were published between 1905 and 1909 (XV, 186, 267, 276; XVI, 54, 523, 529; XVII, 571; XVIII, 52, 205; XIX, 133, 305). Statistical measures of profit, the impact of inventions on interest, and Pigou's views on consumer's surplus and the measurement of elasticity of demand were described in 1910 (XX, 358, 465, 530, 636). Between 1911 and 1913, price discrimination, utility, taxation, and price changes were examined statistically or mathematically (XXI, 139; XXIII, 25, 483, 514, 619), and in 1914 (XXIV, 212) the elasticity of demand for wheat was estimated (by Lehfeld).

Conclusion

Quantitative method has had a place in economics for some two hundred and fifty years. It has grown in importance, particularly during and after the last quarter of the nineteenth century. The use of statistics increased more rapidly than the use of mathematics. Before 1800 the founders of the science, together with their predecessors, the political arithmeticians, made considerable use of quantitative data and of arithmetical illustrations. The small number of pre-1800 writers who made some use of mathematics exercised no influence. In fact, despite the notable work of Cournot and Von

Thünen, and the publications of other capable writers, the mathematical method did not really begin to come into its own until the last quarter of the nineteenth century. Meanwhile, however, statistical and arithmetical matter seems to have come into ever wider use, in part as a result of the stimulus that statistics in general received from the various organizations established in and after the 1830's to promote quantitative work.

Nevertheless, until near the end of the nineteenth century, economics, as generally practiced and envisaged, remained predominantly verbal in composition, with some quantitative and even mathematical matter to be found here and there, but in articles and occasional books rather than in textbooks. The closing decade of the nineteenth century witnessed great improvements in statistical method and a widening appreciation of the contributions mathematical methods might make, with the result that the advent of World War I found many economists ready to incorporate both approaches. This incorporation really began after the war, undergoing rapid acceleration with the development of macroeconomics in the 1930's.

The rate at which economics was quantified was affected by many circumstances, whose distinct contributions are difficult to isolate and assess. Undoubtedly, lack of mathematical and statistical training on the part of economists, together with their inability to emulate practitioners of some natural sciences and to compel fledglings to acquire this training, greatly retarded the quantification of economics, even as it retards it today. Lack of data also checked quantification significantly. It was in demography and in actuarial science, both well supplied with data, that the greatest progress was initially made. Economists, by contrast, were much less well supplied with data, particularly nonprice data, until later in the nineteenth century; moreover, they made insufficient use of what they did have. The introduction of quantitative method was variously affected, but not finally checked, by the canons of inquiry dominant in the several schools of economics. That, by the 1890's, economists were ready to adopt newer methods is suggested by the rapidity with which advanced statistical techniques were put to work.

Additional inferences are supported by our historical review. (1) Factors exogenous to economics were sometimes more important than endogenous factors in fixing the pace of quantification between 1750 and 1920. For the strength of the tendency of economists to deal quantitatively with their subject matter often depended on the conceptions they had of economics, of the questions to be asked, and of the role of economics in public and private affairs; and these circumstances at times even conditioned some of the endogenous factors. Still, some of the endogenous factors were quite important. The availability of data and the extent of economists' quantitative training have been noticed. Equally important were the economic role assigned to the state and the extent to which societies were structurally differentiated. Of some importance also was the prevailing cultural and philosophical *Weltanschauung*, the example of other sciences, and the changing state of mathematics and statistics. (2) Quantification did not always proceed at the same rate in all branches of economics, in part because data were more available in some than in others and quantification was easier, and in part because the interest of economists in various branches of economics varied at different times. (3) The quantitatively empirical did not tend to become merged with the quantitatively abstract until economists with strong empirical interests had attained a high degree of technical proficiency (e.g., H. L. Moore, I. Fisher). (4) The quantification of economics always lagged behind its qualitative and conceptual improvement, though attempts at quantification often sharpened the definition of concepts and facilitated their transformation into an instrument of analysis. (5) The rate at which economics underwent quantification increased in the course of the century, though with little variation until after the 1880's, when the appearance of a number of very able economists accelerated this rate appreciably. (6) The introduction of quantitative methods into economics did not result in striking discoveries or in striking failures, partly because quantification proceeded gradually and partly because economics is not subject to crucial experiments. (7) Quantification rendered economics increasingly more exact at both the theoretical and the empirical levels, and it may even have transformed it. The accumulation of small changes over more than a century made the economics of 1920 (as it did that of 1950) quite unlike that of 1750 to 1830.

NOTES

1. See, e.g., S. Moos, "Laissez Faire, Planning and Ethics," *Economic Journal,* LV (1945), 17–27; L. Robbins, *The Theory of Economic Policy in English Classical Political Economy,* London, 1952; S. G. Checkland, "The Advent of Academic Economics in England," *Manchester School,* XIX (1951), 43–70.

2. It has been said that a period during which quantification was asserted to be necessary, though not practiced, tended to be followed by one during which great enthusiasm for quantification was manifested. There usually followed a period during which opposition to quantification became strong and its results were depreciated, with the consequence that disillusion respecting the usefulness of quantitative methods became dominant for a time. In the end, however, the actual role of quantitative method tended to become fairly commensurate with its potentialities.

3. On this question as it arises in the field of science in general, see R. K. Merton, "Priorities in Scientific Discovery: A Chapter in the Sociology of Science," *American Sociological Review,* XXII (1957), 635–659; also Bernard Barber, *Science and the Social Order,* Glencoe, 1952, *passim.*

4. Attention will be devoted largely to consciously constructed models, since one may then be reasonably certain about what the author of the model intended. When one reduces an early author's argument to terms of a model, or when one makes explicit what at most was an implicit model, one usually reads into an author's argument far more than he intended, and one is likely to assess incorrectly the inferences that he drew. As H. Bergson remarked (*Two Sources of Morality and Religion;* Garden City, N.Y., 1954, p. 308), "We, who know what followed, cannot help transferring back the image of it to the beginning."

5. See the papers on Greek, Roman, medieval, and early modern accounting, particularly those by G. E. M. de Ste. Croix and R. de Roover, in A. C. Littleton and B. S. Yamey, *Studies in the History of Accounting,* Homewood, Ill., 1956. Ste. Croix infers that, in Europe, although accounts were "kept mainly in Roman figures until at least the sixteenth century," the introduction of Arabic numerals in the twelfth century stimulated the development of double entry. See *ibid.,* pp. 62–64; see also text and note 6 below on nonaccounting data.

6. Although many censuses, complete or partial, had been taken at irregular intervals before the closing decade of the eighteenth century, it was not until this time that regularly recurring and complete enumerative censuses began to be taken, and then not in many countries until after the middle of the nineteenth century. See J. Koren (ed.), *The History of Statistics,* New York, 1918; A. B. Wolfe, "Population Censuses before 1790," *Journal of the American Statistical Association,* XXVII, (1932), 357–370; Helen M. Walker, *Studies in the History of Statistical Method,* Baltimore, 1929, pp. 32–38; P. G. Edge, "Early Population Records of Spain," *Metron,* IX (1932), 222–249; R. S.

Smith, "Fourteenth-Century Population Records of Catalonia," *Speculum,* XIX (1944), 494–501; J. Krause, "The Medieval Household: Large or Small?" *Economic History Review,* IX (1957), 420–432; H. E. Hallam, "Some Thirteenth-Century Censuses," *ibid.,* X (1958), 340–361; W. F. Wilcox, *Studies in American Demography,* Ithaca, N.Y., 1940, *passim;* J. J. Spengler, *France Faces Depopulation,* Durham, N.C., 1938; D. V. Glass, "The Population Controversy in Eighteenth-Century England," *Population Studies,* VI (1952), 69–91, esp. 83–87.

7. See F. Meinecke, *Machiavellism,* London, 1957, p. 121; J. A. Schumpeter, *History of Economic Analysis,* New York, 1954, ch. 3. S. Münster's *Cosmographia* appeared in 1536, and N. Froumenteau's *Le secret des finances de France découvert et départi en trois livres,* in 1581. On the origin of the term *statistics* see V. John, *Geschichte der Statistik,* Stuttgart, 1884, pp. 3–14, and "The Term 'Statistics,'" *Journal of the Royal Statistical Society* (hereinafter designated *JRSS*), XLVI (1883), 656–679; G. U. Yule, "The Introduction of the Words 'Statistics,' 'Statistical,' into the English Language," *JRSS,* LXVIII (1905), 391–396; Willcox, *op. cit.,* pp. 491–510; and F. Zizek's comments thereon in International Statistical Institute, *Revue* (where Willcox's essay first appeared), VI (1938), 519–552.

8. See John, *op. cit.,* pp. 34–54; W. Lexis, "Statistik," in *Handwoerterbuch der Staatswissenschaften,* 3d ed., VIII, Jena, 1911, pp. 824–832; C. A. Verrijn Stuart, *Inleiding tot de Boefening der Statistiek,* I, Haarlem, 1910, p. 75; the article "Statistique," in *Dictionnaire de l'économie politique,* II, Paris, 1864, pp. 653–666 and in *Nouveau dictionnaire de l'économie politique,* II, Paris, 1900, pp. 911–921; L. Cossa, *An Introduction to the Study of Political Economy,* London, 1893, *passim;* H. Westergaard, *Contributions to the History of Statistics,* London, 1932, pp. 1–15; A. Meitzen, *History, Theory, and Technique of Statistics* (trans. R. P. Falkner), which appeared as a supplement to Vol. I of the *Annals* of the American Academy of Political and Social Science, 1891, pp. 18–24, 36–37, 75 ff., 90 ff., 166 ff. Illustrative of this tendency to include relatively little quantitative matter are works of August L. Schlözer (*Theories der Statistik,* Göttingen, 1804), and J. G. Meusel (*Litteratur der Statistik,* Leipzig, 1790; *Lehrbuch der Statistik,* Leipzig, 1817), who described the subject matter of *Staatskunde* or *Statistik* (a term apparently first used by Achenwall, though long after Helenus Politanus used the term *statisticum* in 1672) much as had Conring and Achenwall (*ibid.,* pp. 1–10); and C. A. von Malchus (*Statistik und Staatenkunde,* Stuttgart, 1826). While J. Fallati (*Einleitung in die Wissenschaft der Statistik,* Tübingen, 1843) presents a somewhat modified conception of statistics (but no tabular matter), Moritz Fränzel (*Statistik,* Wien, 1838, 1841) includes considerable quantitative as well as descriptive matter for many countries ("Die Statistik ist die Schilderung der Staaten, aus dem politischen Gesichtspunkte," *ibid.,* I, p. 1), and G. F. Kolb (*Handbuch der vergleichenden Statistik,* Leipzig, 1868) introduces a great deal of internationally comparative and other statistical information. P. A. Dufau (*Traité de statistique,* Paris, 1840) conceived of the end of statistics as the discovery

of the laws that govern social phenomena; but, as late as 1856, A. Moreau de Jonnes (*Eléments de statistique,* Paris, 1856) was describing it as "a science of facts, like history," and as late as 1875 the *Programmes de l'enseignement intérieur de l'école des ponts et chausses* (Paris, 1875, pp. 28–29) was stressing the conduct of inquiries and the gathering of data. Statistical as well as straight descriptive matter entered into early nineteenth-century geographical works. See, e.g., C. G. D. Stein's *Handbuch der Geographie und Statistik* (rev. by F. Horschelmann), 3 vols. Leipzig, 1833–34.

9. Carl G. A. Knies used this term to distinguish authors in the Conring-Achenwall-Schlözer tradition from those who viewed the office of statistics (as did Knies) as the exact, quantitative, and mathematical investigation of social phenomena. See *Die Statistik als selbstständige Wissenschaft,* Kassel, 1850, esp. pp. 168 ff. Knies reviews the historical development of statistics and then analyzes critically the approaches of the main schools. See note 223 below.

10. See John, *op. cit.,* pp. 123–133, esp. p. 129; Westergaard, *op. cit.,* pp. 14–15; Meitzen, *op. cit.,* pp. 41, 90–92. This essentially literary approach to descriptive data did not, however, prevent some of its exponents from supporting demands for the assembly and publication of quantitative materials. On the development of official statistics before 1800, see *ibid.,* pp. 24–55; and on the state of official statistics around 1800, Westergaard, *op. cit.,* ch. 11.

11. See F. H. Hankins, *Adolphe Quételet as Statistician,* New York, 1908, pp. 41 ff.; also Meitzen, *op. cit.,* pp. 91–92.

12. See Westergaard, *op. cit.,* pp. 136, 139–143; Meitzen, *op. cit.,* pp. 50–53; P. J. Fitzpatrick, "Statistical Societies in the United States in the Nineteenth Century," *American Statistician,* XI(5), 1957, 13–21; also "Leading British Statisticians of the Nineteenth Century," *Journal of the American Statistical Association,* LV (1960), 38–70; and "Leading Statisticians of the Nineteenth Century," *ibid.,* LII (1957), 301–321; LIII (1958), 689–701.

13. In the new journal of the London or Royal Statistical Society, statistics is described as a link between particular sciences and "the practical purposes of life." See *JRSS,* I (1838), 2. "It is simply required that all conclusions shall be drawn from well-attested data, and shall admit of mathematical demonstration" (*ibid.,* p. 3). "The Science of Statistics differs from Political Economy, because, although it has the same end in view, it does not discuss causes, nor reason upon probable effects; it seeks only to collect, arrange, and compare, that class of facts which alone can form the basis of correct conclusions with respect to social and political government" (*ibid.,* p. 1). According to the Report of the General Secretaries, in the then stage of development of political economy, the "science" of statistics was related to economics as "astronomical observations" had been related to astronomy "before the discoveries of mechanical philosophy enabled recent philosophers to make these early observations perform a mighty part in testing the great primal truths of physical philosophy," applying them to explain, and even to predict, the varied motions and phenomena of the "earth and heavens." In this "inductive" stage,

there was need for "observation without premature speculation" (see *ibid.*, p. 322). T. C. D. Lawson cautioned, however, lest the principles of political economy be unduly disregarded. "While statistics afford materials and a test to political economy, the latter points out the proper object of statistical inquiry, and draws conclusions from their results." See "On the Connexion between Statistics and Political Economy," *ibid.*, VI (1843), 322. Probably the best index of change in the content and role of statistics is the content of the papers published, summarized, or reviewed in the *Journal of the Royal Statistical Society;* late nineteenth-century changes in methods, etc., are reflected there. Changes are reflected also in the *Journal des économistes* (which began in 1842) and in the *Journal de la société de statistique de Paris* (which began in 1860). J. M. Keynes observed "that the business of statistical technique ought to be regarded as strictly limited to preparing the numerical aspects of our material in an intelligible form, so as to be ready for the application of the usual inductive methods." It was not the business of this technique "to turn its results into probabilities" (see *A Treatise on Probability,* London, 1921, p. 392). See also K. E. Boulding's skepticism concerning the use to be made of statistical matter in complicated, dynamic studies, in his "In Defense of Statistics," *Quarterly Journal of Economics,* LXIX (1955), 499–502. On the early approaches see also Fitzpatrick's works, cited in note 12.

14. In a work then (1924) representative of the best of the essentially nonmathematical textbooks on statistical methods for economists, F. C. Mills dealt with graphic presentation, the frequency distribution (i.e., averages and measures of variation of skewness), index numbers of prices and physical volume, the analysis of time series (i.e., trend, seasonal, any cyclical fluctuations), the measurement of relationship (i.e., linear, nonlinear, multiple and partial correlation; the problem of estimation; relationship between time series), elementary probabilities and the normal curve of error, statistical induction and sampling, and the application of the method of least squares. See his *Statistical Methods,* 1st ed., New York, 1924.

15. See Walker, *op. cit.*, pp. 9–11, 27–30. Probability theory as developed by Pascal and Fermat was of the a priori sort. As M. Kline puts it (in a review in *Scientific American,* CXCVIII (May, 1958), 144: "the possible events must be lawless for the laws of a priori probability to apply."

16. Walker, *op. cit.*, pp. 13–17.

17. *Ibid.*, pp. 18–21.

18. *Ibid.*, pp. 21–26, also 49–64 on abscissa units of the normal curve, on probability function tables, and probable errors. Encke's book "reads much as though it had come from the Pearson laboratory in an early day," writes Walker (*ibid.*, p. 25). Encke's book "served as a basis for numerous textbooks" (*ibid.*, p. 26). A. De Morgan sought "to reduce the theory of probability" and the construction of a normal curve "to rules which might be followed by persons having no command of mathematics beyond simple arithmetic" (*ibid.*, pp. 26–27).

19. *Ibid.*, p. 28. This law was also used in dealing with problems relating to artillery fire.

20. See J. M. Keynes, *A Treatise on Probability*, chs. 28–29; G. U. Yule and M. G. Kendall, *An Introduction to the Theory of Statistics*, 13th ed., London, 1949, pp. 187–91. Keynes (*op. cit.*, p. 336) preferred "Stability of Statistical Frequencies" to "Law of Great Numbers."

21. See his *Physique sociale, ou essai sur le développement des facultés de l'homme*, Brussels, 1869 (a new edition of his *Sur l'homme*, Paris, 1835); *Du système sociale et des lois que le régissent*, Paris, 1848. See also Hankins, *op. cit.*; M. Halbwachs, *La théorie de l'homme moyen: Essai sur Quételet et la statistique morale*, Paris, 1913.

22. See Hankins, *op. cit.*, pp. 56–57, 88–89, 98 ff.; John, *op. cit.*, pp. 332–370. Condorcet and Laplace had been interested in problems of elections and moral behavior, but they did not interest themselves in the theory of economic welfare as such. See Duncan Black, *The Theory of Committees and Elections*, Cambridge, 1958, pp. 159–185.

23. On Quételet's application of the "normal law," see Hankins, *op. cit.*, pp. 77–78, 126–127; also J. Venn, *Logic of Chance*, 3rd ed., London, 1888, ch. 2. See also L. Hogben's criticism of Quételet's assumptions, in *Statistical Theory*, New York, 1957, Pt. II; Keynes, *op. cit.*, pp. 334–335, 393. Although many Germans opposed Quételet's determinism, he greatly stimulated German university statistics, according to John (*op. cit.*, p. 370).

24. See Keynes, *op. cit.*, pp. 392–401. On the matter of discrepancy between normal and other distributions and on methods of accommodating statistical theory thereto, see Yule and Kendall, *op. cit.*, pp. 185–187; A. L. Bowley, *F. Y. Edgeworth's Contributions to Mathematical Statistics*, London, 1928; Hogben, *op. cit.*, ch. 7; Keynes, *op. cit.*, ch. 7; F. Zizek, *Statistical Averages* (trans. W. M. Persons), New York, 1913, pp. 253 ff., 276–291. Zizek's book, though rich in references, contains very little numerical matter.

25. As late as 1906 A. L. Bowley remarked that despite the improvement in the data available, there had been "remarkably little application" of the recently developed methods to "practical statistical problems." See report of address in *JRSS*, LXIX (1906), 541, 548; also *ibid.*, LXXI (1908), 459 ff. on needed improvements in official statistics. See also W. M. Persons, *Forecasting Business Cycles*, New York, 1931, ch. 16; and F. F. Stephan, "History of the Uses of Modern Sampling Procedure," *Journal of the American Statistical Association*, XLIII (1948), 12–39.

26. See Bowley, *F. Y. Edgeworth's Contributions*, pp. 1–5 and pp. 129–139, where are listed 74 papers published between 1883 and 1926. When Edgeworth began writing, "very little interest was taken in any but objective statistics" except in actuarial science and the treatment of some vital statistical data (*ibid.*, pp. 1–2). Illustrative of the latter view are W. F. Farr's emphasis (*JRSS*, XXVII [1864], 459–478) upon comparative data; W. A. Guy's opinion (*ibid.*, XXVIII [1865], 478–493) that political economy was a branch of statistics and sociology (*ibid.*, XLIV [1881], 36–48; XLIX [1886], 736–754); etc. In "Meth-

ods of Statistics" (in *Jubilee Volume of the Statistical Society*, London, 1885, pp. 181–217), a paper incorporating the best of current statistical theory, Edgeworth dealt with the comparison of means, the law of error and its genesis and use, the determination of the spread of the curve as indicated by its modulus, and the application of the calculus of probabilities to anthropometrical, vital-statistical, banking, and other data, and to concatenations of comparisons. For a comparison of the Edgeworthian and the Pearsonian systems, each of which is "based on variants from the law of error," see Bowley, *op. cit.*, pp. 81–85. See below on Edgeworth's economic writings. The standard deviation δ came to perform the function at first assigned to the modulus, $\delta\sqrt{2}$.

27. See, e.g., J. G. Mandello, "The Future of Statistics," *JRSS*, LXVIII (1905), 725–732; also J. B. Martin, "On Some Developments of Statistical Research and Methods during Recent Years," *ibid.*, LIX (1896), 579–628. A. de Foville pointed, however, to the limitations of statistics (*ibid.*, LI [1888], 162 ff.; LXVIII [1905], 733 ff.).

28. Walker, *op. cit.*, pp. 81–88, 184, 186–188; J. Venn, "On the Nature and Use of Averages," *JRSS*, LIV (1891), 429–448; Bowley, *Elements of Statistics*, London, 1901, chs. 5–6, and *Edgeworth's Contributions*, pp. 10 ff., 59, 131, 133, 137–138; Zizek, *op. cit.*, H. Higgs, "Workmen's Budgets," *JRSS*, LVI, (1893), 255–285, and Edgeworth's comments on Higgs's use of an average family after the practice of Le Play (*ibid.*, pp. 670–675). See also W. S. Jevons, *The Principles of Science* (1877), London, 1924, chs. 16–17; *Investigations in Currency and Finance*, 1884, pp. 120 ff.; and "On the Variations of Prices and the Value of the Currency Since 1782," *JRSS*, XXVIII (1865), 294–320. Concerning Galton's early use of percentiles, quartiles, etc., see Walker, *op. cit.*, pp. 84, 88, 186–187, and his comments on Yule's methods in *JRSS*, LIX (1896), 392–398. Bowley dealt with the accuracy of an average a year later (*JRSS*, LX, 855–866), and J. M. Keynes, with averages and the law of error, in 1911 (*ibid.*, LXXIV, 322–331).

29. Walker, *op. cit.*, ch. 3, pp. 184–186.

30. E.g., on removing cyclical fluctuations see Jevons, *A Serious Fall in the Value of Gold*, London, 1836, pp. 15–16, and on seasonal variation, his *Investigations in Currency and Finance*, pp. 3–11, 160 ff.

31. A physicist, J. H. Poynting, who used four- and ten-year moving averages to get rid of "accidental irregularities" and to discover the extent to which prices fluctuated together, discussed the degree to which his method of averaging got rid of harmonics of different lengths. See "A Comparison of the Fluctuations in the Price of Wheat and in the Cotton and Silk Imports into Great Britain," *JRSS*, XLVII (1884), 36–47. In this paper, H. T. Davis notes, Poynting originated the variate-difference method (*The Analysis of Economic Time Series*, Bloomington, Ind., 1941, pp. 240–241). Poynting's work was praised highly by Edgeworth (*Economic Journal*, IV [1894], 159–160).

32. See also, e.g., Bowley, *Elements*, pp. 151–156, 175 ff., 178 ff., 199; W. F. Sheppard, "On the Use of Auxiliary Curves in Statistics of Continuous Variation," *JRSS*, LXIII (1900), 433–458, 637–648.

33. Persons, *op. cit.*, p. 256. For an earlier quantitative approach to trade-cycle analysis see C. Juglar, *Des crises commerciales,* 2d ed., Paris, 1889. Juglar's earliest work was done in the 1850's.

34. See Bowley, *JRSS*, LXIX (1906), 549–557; also *Elements,* 3d ed., pp. 308 ff.; and Westergaard, *op. cit.*, pp. 263 ff. On early uses of sampling and the development and adoption of systematic sampling techniques in the present century, see Stephan, *op. cit.*

35. Walker, *op. cit.*, pp. 97–98, 104–112, 175–179, 181, 185–187; bibliography on pp. 130–141; also p. 189 on Pearson's description (in 1907) of the variate-difference method of computing correlation as having "long been in use as an alternative to the product-moment method." Pearson published his first fundamental paper in 1896, and Yule his, "On the Theory of Correlation" (*JRSS*, LX [1897], 812–854), a year later. Edgeworth had published six papers in 1892–94 (Bowley, *Edgeworth's Contributions,* pp. 133–134). See also Yule, "The Applications of the Method of Correlation to Social and Economic Statistics," *JRSS*, LXXII (1909), 722–723, and bibliography, pp. 729–730; and Bowley, *Elements,* Pt. II. Yule also dealt with correlation and association in *JRSS*, LXXIII (1910), 644–647; LXXV (1912), 579–642.

36. Walker, *op. cit.*, pp. 126–131. Yule's work was based partly on that of Jevons, who had been stimulated by Boole (*ibid.*, pp. 126–127).

37. See his notes in the *Economic Journal,* V (1895), 603; VI (1896), 613; and his papers in *JRSS*, LIX (1896), 318–349, and LXII (1899), 249–286. The first of these Yule describes as "the first case of economic interest to which the theory of correlation was applied" (*JRSS*, LXXII [1909], p. 723).

38. "On the Correlation of the Marriage-Rate with Trade," *JRSS*, LXIV (1901), 485–492. Hooker states that "comparatively little use" had so far been made of correlation, etc., "in the domain of economics" (*ibid.*, pp. 485 ff.). Yule summarizes studies by L. March and by himself (*JRSS*, LXXII [1902], 725–726) dealing with economic and vital-statistical fluctuations. See also his study of the factors affecting English marriage and birth rates (*JRSS*, LXIX, [1906], 88–132).

39. "The Suspension of the Berlin Produce Exchange and Its Effect upon Corn Prices," *JRSS*, LXIV (1901), 574–604; "On the Correlation of Successive Observations, Illustrated by Corn Prices," *ibid.*, LXVIII (1905), 696 ff. (with G. U. Yule), "Note on Estimating the Relative Influence of Two Variables on a Third," *ibid.*, LXIX (1906), 197–200. In the second of these papers Hooker deals (as in his paper cited in note 38) with elimination of "secular" change. S. J. Chapman and D. Knoop made use of some of the newer methods in "Dealings in Futures and the Cotton Market," *JRSS*, LXIX (1906), 321–364; they commented respecting the limitations of various methods of analysis.

40. See J. P. Norton, *Statistical Studies in the New York Money Market,* New York, 1902; A. Lee, "On the Manner in Which the Percentage of Unemployed Workmen in This Country Is Related to the Import of Articles Wholly or Mainly Manufactured," *Economic Journal,* XVIII (1908), 96 ff. Norton used a logarithmic curve instead of a moving average. In his work,

dealing with a form of seasonal variation in the money market that had interested Jevons, he used a method for determining lag discovered independently by Wood (see Bowley, *Economic Journal,* XII [1902], 516–517).

41. See the section on quantitative methods in economics before 1800, below, on the early history of graphs.

42. See his *Principles of Science* (1874), 3d ed., London, 1924, pp. 492–495, on graphic method. According to H. G. Funkhouser, coordinate paper was used as early as 1800, but it remained unfamiliar as late as 1879. L. Lalanne drew logarithmic grids as early as 1843. See Funkhouser, "Historical Development of the Graphical Representation of Statistical Data," *Osiris,* III (1937), 269–404, esp. 343, 359. In *Traité des valeurs mobilières* (1870), M. H. Lefèvre used coordinate diagrams to represent various combinations of operations on stock or produce exchanges. See the article "Polegraphy" in Palgrave's *Dictionary of Political Economy,* II, London, 1926, pp. 120–124.

43. Funkhouser, *op. cit.,* pp. 359–360, 384. See Jevons, *A Serious Fall in the Value of Gold Ascertained, and Its Social Effects Set Forth, with Two Diagrams,* London, 1863. Jevons used many graphs in his *Investigations in Currency and Finance,* in which also are found his well-known index numbers.

44. See E. Levasseur, "La statistique graphique," in the *Jubilee Volume of the Statistical Society,* pp. 218–250; A. Marshall, "On the Graphic Method of Statistics," *ibid.,* pp. 251–262, reprinted in *Memorials of Alfred Marshall* (ed. A. C. Pigou), London, 1925, pp. 175–187. This method, which permitted employment of Whewell's inductive "method of curves," facilitated grasp of detail, comparison, and discovery of longer-run movements, according to J. N. Keynes. See his *The Scope and Method of Political Economy,* 4th ed., London, 1917, pp. 339–341. This edition does not differ greatly from the first or 1890 edition.

45. See Palgrave's *Dictionary of Political Economy,* II, pp. 251–255.

46. See "The Ratio Chart for Plotting Statistics," *Publications of the American Statistical Association,* XV (1916–17), 577–601. See also E. A. Goldenweiser's critique of the quality of graphical analysis, in "Classification and Limitations of Statistical Graphics," *ibid.,* pp. 205–209; J. A. Field, "Some Advantages of the Logarithmic Scale in Statistical Diagrams," *Journal of Political Economy,* XXV (1917), 805–841; and A. L. Bowley, *Elements,* ch. 7. Funkhouser (*op. cit.,* p. 361) and Fisher cite a number of works dealing with graphic method.

47. In the eighteenth century, price averages were used by W. Fleetwood, Dutot, N. F. Dupré de Saint-Maur, G. R. Carli, and G. S. Evelyn; between 1800 and 1850, by Arthur Young, J. P. Smith, Joseph Lowe, Henry James, G. R. Porter, M. C. Leber, and G. C. Scrope, formulator of the "tabular standard." See C. M. Walsh, *The Measurement of General Exchange Value,* New York, 1901, pp. 533–556. The now well-known Paasche type of index was suggested, along with the more general Scrope type, as early as 1828, but nothing came of the suggestion. See R. W. Jastram, "Willard Phillips, a Predecessor of Paasche in Index Number Formulation," *Journal of the American*

Statistical Association, XLVI (1951), 124–126. Phillips, and not Scrope, seems to have been the first to introduce the subject of index numbers into a general text, his work appearing in 1828 and Scrope's in 1833. Index numbers are not employed in George Tucker's *Progress of the United States in Population and Wealth in Fifty Years,* Philadelphia, 1843, considered by some "the most important American book on statistics" to appear before 1850. See P. J. Fitzpatrick, "Statistical Works in Early American Statistics Courses," *American Statistician,* X(5), 1956, 14–19. In his *The Science of Wealth,* Boston, 1866, Amasa Walker employed Dutot's method (Walsh, *op. cit.,* p. 558). On earlier British price indexes see A. D. Gayer *et al., The Growth and Fluctuation of the British Economy, 1790–1850,* Oxford, 1953, pp. 517–528; this work also includes considerable information on sources of data.

48. Walsh lists works by A. Soetbeer, J. Maclaren, E. Levasseur, W. Newmarch, W. S. Jevons, E. Laspeyres, A. Walker, Ph. Geyer, M. W. Drobisch, W. Roscher, H. Paasche, A. Hanauer, A. Ellis, R. Griffin, S. Bourne, A. de Foville, and A. Messadaglia. See Walsh, *op. cit.,* pp. 556–562, also 532–553; he refers to many eighteenth- and nineteenth-century writers on value and its measure.

49. Walsh (*ibid.,* pp. 562–574) lists about fifty authors who wrote on index numbers and their construction between 1881 and 1900. See also Westergaard, *op. cit.,* pp. 202–207, 265–266; Edgeworth, "Index Numbers," in Palgrave's *Dictionary of Political Economy,* II, pp. 384–388; A. Sauerbeck, "Prices of Commodities and the Precious Metals," *JRSS,* XLIX (1886), 541–648; A. Ellis, "The Quantification of Stock Exchange Values," *JRSS,* LI (1888), 567–589.

50. See I. Fisher, *Purchasing Power of Money,* New York, 1911, and *The Making of Index Numbers,* Boston, 1922; W. C. Mitchell, *Index Numbers of Wholesale Prices in the United States and Foreign Countries,* U.S.B.L.S. Bulletin 173, Washington, 1915; C. M. Walsh, *The Fundamental Problem in Monetary Science,* New York, 1903, *The Problem of Estimation,* London, 1921, and "Index Numbers," in *Encyclopedia of the Social Sciences,* VII, New York, 1932, pp. 652–658; L. L. Laughlin, *The Principles of Money,* Chicago, 1903, ch. 6; F. Y. Edgeworth, *Papers Relating to Political Economy,* I, London, 1925, sec. 3; Bowley, *Edgeworth's Contributions;* A. A. Young, *Economic Problems New and Old,* Boston, 1927, chs. 13–14, and his contribution to H. L. Rietz (ed.), *Handbook of Mathematical Statistics,* Boston, 1924, pp. 181–194; J. M. Keynes, *A Treatise on Money,* New York, 1930, Bk. II; Zizek, *op. cit.,* pp. 95–101, 156 ff. Among the students of the value of money, E. W. Kemmerer may be cited for his work on seasonal variation, in *Seasonal Variations in the Relative Demand for Money and Capital in the United States,* Washington, 1910. In his *Purchasing Power,* Fisher dealt with averages, the equation of exchange, and the attributes of various index numbers.

51. Schumpeter, *History,* p. 1093. Elsewhere (*ibid.,* p. 1089 *n.*) he says that "index numbers imposed themselves upon the profession as a whole by a slow process of infiltration." W. C. Mitchell's work does not wholly answer to Schumpeter's description; his concepts were shaped in part by his extensive

knowledge of the statistics descriptive of the behavior of the American and other economies. See Arthur F. Burns, *Wesley Clair Mitchell, the Economic Scientist,* New York, 1952, pp. 4–54.

52. See articles in Palgrave's *Dictionary of Political Economy,* II, pp. 509–511, 639–646, 674–679, 797–803.

53. See, e.g., particularly the series of papers by A. L. Bowley (sometimes with G. H. Wood as co-author) in *JRSS,* LVIII (1895); LXI–LXV (1898–1902); LXVIII–LXIX (1905–6). See also Bowley, *Elements,* 3d ed., pp. 178–187, dealing with elimination of seasonal variation; G. H. Wood, "Some Statistics Relating to Working Class Progress Since 1860," *JRSS,* LXII (1899), 639–666; Bowley and Edgeworth, "Methods of Representing Statistics of Wages and Other Groups Not Fulfilling the Normal Law of Error," *JRSS,* LXV (1902), 325–354, and Bowley, "A Suggestion for the International Comparison of Wages by the Use of the Median," *JRSS,* LXXII (1909), 718–721. Statistical analysis led R. H. Hooker to conclude that the supply of labor is a function of wages. See "On the Relations between Wages and the Numbers Employed in the Coal Mining Industry," *JRSS,* LVII (1894), 627–642.

54. E.g., on indexes in use early in the present century, see Bowley, *Elements,* 3d ed., pp. 159–177; G. François, "Les crises et la statistique," *Revue d'économie politique,* XXII (1908), 542–550; M. T. Copeland, "Statistical Indices of Business Conditions," *Quarterly Journal of Economics,* XXIX (1914–15), 522–562. See also Westergaard, *op. cit.,* pp. 204–207 on late nineteenth-century proposals of Fr. X. Neumann-Spallart and others on such indices.

55. See Vols. I–III, 1919–21, esp. the papers by W. M. Persons and E. E. Day. Four types of fluctuation—secular, cyclical, seasonal, and residual—are identified. See also Persons, *Forecasting Business Cycles.*

56. See, e.g., H. T. Davis, *op. cit.,* ch. I, on history of the time-series problem.

57. See e.g., H. S. Pritchett, "A Formula for Predicting the Population of the United States," *Publications of the American Statistical Association* (hereafter denoted by *PASA*), II (1891), 278–286; E. Cannan, *Economic Scares,* London, 1933, pp. 108–135, for papers published in 1895 and 1901, in which careful projections based on observed trends were made.

58. See R. Pearl, *Medical Biometry and Statistics,* 3d ed., Philadelphia, 1940, ch. 18; also ch. 2, on "some landmarks in the history of biostatistics." While Edgeworth was inclined to consider the a priori validity of the assumptions underlying a curve, he favored, when the "law of progress" characteristic of a series was not known but presumably small, use of an arithmetic progression as a good approximation (see Bowley, *Edgeworth's Contributions,* pp. 65–66, 96–97).

59. E.g., R. D. Prescott found the Gompertz curve descriptive of the growth of industries ("Law of Growth in Forecasting Demand," *Journal of the American Statistical Association,* XVIII (1922), 471–479); S. Kuznets found it and the simple logistic descriptive of the long-time growth of industries (*Secular Movements in Production and Prices,* Boston, 1930, pp. 197–199). See also papers cited in my essay in S. Kuznets (ed.), *Problems in the Study of Economic*

Growth (*NBER*), New York, 1949, pp. 47–116. The Gompertz curve was originally devised in 1825 to deal with the exhaustion of man's power to avoid death (see Westergaard, *op. cit.*, pp. 129 ff.).

60. See, e.g., E. F. de Flaix's and W. J. Harris' accounts of the growth of wealth in France and England (*JRSS*, XLIX [1886], 186–200; LVII [1894], 524–555); R. Giffen's reports on material and related progress (in which he anticipates Colin Clark when he says that industry "everywhere" follows "the law of becoming more miscellaneous" [*JRSS*, L (1887), 615–647, esp. 645; LI (1888), 713–805; LIII (1890), 1–35]); G. J. Goschen's finding that income distribution was becoming less unequal (*JRSS*, L [1887], 495–541). Many papers were in the pattern of those cited.

61. See Pareto, *Cours d'économie politique*, Lausanne, 1897, II, Bk. 3, ch. 1; C. Gini, "The Contributions of Italy to Modern Statistical Methods," *JRSS*, LXXXIX (1926), 709–724; M. O. Lorenz, "Methods of Measuring the Concentration of Wealth," *PASA*, IX (1905), 202–209; U. Ricci, *L'indici di concentrazione e di dipendenza*, Rome, 1916; R. Gibrat, *Les inégalités économiques*, Paris, 1931; Zizek, *op. cit.*, pp. 348–350. For accounts and assessments of these and later measures, see C. Bresciani-Turroni, "Annual Survey of Statistical Data: Pareto's Law and the Index of Inequality of Incomes," *Econometrica*, VIII (1939), 107–133; M. J. Bowman, "A Graphical Analysis of Personal Income Distribution in the United States," *American Economic Review*, XXXV (1945), 607–628; D. B. Yntema, "Measures of Inequality in the Personal Distribution of Wealth or Income," *Journal of the American Statistical Association*, XXVIII (1928), 423–433; H. T. Davis, *op. cit.*, ch. 9; Funkhouser, "Historical Development . . . ," pp. 362–364. For many references to Pareto's curve see Edgeworth's account in Palgrave's *Dictionary of Political Economy*, III, pp. 711–712, and the *Giornale degli Economisti*, LXIV (1924), 1–153.

62. "An Interpretation of Certain Statistical Evidence of Concentration of Wealth," *PASA*, XI (1907–8), 27–55; "The Measurement of Concentration of Wealth," *Quarterly Journal of Economics*, XXIV (1910–11), 160–179. Just as Lorenz had found the methods of Goschen and J. Wolf fallacious and G. K. Holme's use of means and medians ("Measures of Distribution," *PASA*, III [1893], 141–157) inadequate, so had Watkins found Lorenz' curve and the coefficient of variation less satisfactory than a log-log curve. Watkins indicated that his curve was not inspired by Pareto's.

63. "The Variability in the Distribution of Wealth and Income," *Quarterly Journal of Economics*, XXIII (1909–10), 416–449, and his comment upon Watkins' paper, *ibid.*, XXIV (1910–11), 179–190. H. L. Moore used the coefficient of variation in "The Variability of Wages," *Political Science Quarterly*, XXII (1907), 61–73. Young, *op. cit.*, ch. 6, reviewed various measures, to which he preferred a simple frequency distribution. See also Bresciani-Turroni, *op. cit.*, pp. 117–118, on the view of Schmoller, held in part also by E. Engel,

that the distribution of income, though subject to variation in the short run, tended to be stable in the long run.

64. See Bowley, *Elements,* 3d ed., p. 136; Lorenz, *op. cit.,* p. 215; Persons, "The Variability . . . ," p. 421; A. E. James, "The Dewey Report on Wages in Manufacturing Industries in the United States," *PASA,* X (1906–7), p. 336.

65. In *Publications of the American Economic Association,* III (1888).

66. *Traité théorique et pratique de statistique,* Paris, 1878.

67. Meitzen, *op. cit.,* Pt. II. "Theoretical statistics is the doctrine of a strictly systematic process of investigation which can be properly applied to every concrete object conceived as complex and changeable" (*ibid.,* p. 211).

68. *Storia e teoria generale della statistica,* 1st ed., Milan, 1880. Gabaglio took it for granted that the manner in which statistics were employed in economic analysis was governed by the economic concepts in use. He reviews the history of statistics (as did Meitzen and Block) in Part I, deals with statistical theory and method in Part II, pp. 231 ff., and with the use of graphs, pp. 580 ff. A second edition, in two volumes, appeared in 1888. Gabaglio's manual was the best available, according to W. Hooper, "On the Method of Statistical Analysis," *JRSS,* XLIV (1881), 31–48.

69. W. M. Persons, who, along with I. Fisher and H. L. Moore, played a major role in introducing the newer methods into American economic writings, observed in 1925 that, because "data and methods were lacking," economists gave little attention to statistical studies before the 1880's. "The development of modern statistical methods began" in the 1880's and early 1890's with "the application of the theory of probability to statistics by Lexis and Edgeworth, the invention of correlation analysis by Galton, and its extension by Karl Pearson and others. The general use of index numbers" did not begin until after 1900. The study of "methods strictly adapted to two of the most important, if not the most important, problems of economic statistics—the correlation and periodicity of time-series" did not come until a decade or so later. See his "Statistics and Economic Theory" (1925), included as ch. 16 in *Forecasting Business Cycles,* esp. p. 274. This and other chapters contain much of interest to the student of the history of quantification. See also H. L. Moore, "The Statistical Complement of Pure Economics," *Quarterly Journal of Economics,* XXIII (1908), 1 ff., and *Laws of Wages,* New York, 1911, pp. 1–23. Moore remarked (*ibid.,* pp. 5–6) that at long last "the perfection of mechanical devices for performing mathematical computations" would permit analysis of the mass of data actually or potentially available. W. C. Mitchell's emphasis was not on models or fancy techniques, but on the laborious measurement and analysis of mass observation.

70. See C. P. Sanger's review of Bowley's *Elements* in *Economic Journal,* XI (1901), 193–197; also p. 18 of Fitzpatrick's paper, cited in note 47 above. The first edition of Yule's *Introduction to the Theory of Statistics,* based on his lectures given in 1902–9, was completed in 1910.

71. See Bowley, *Edgeworth's Contributions,* p. 86; Edgeworth's paper is cited in note 26 above.

72. Bowley remarked in 1906 (*JRSS*, LXIX [1906], 543–545) that, with the exception of the University of London, English universities were not making adequate provision for statistical training. See also Yule, *JRSS*, LX (1897), 456–458. Apparently sufficient provision was made for the introduction of advanced methods in Italy and Scandinavia, though not in Germany. See G. Seibt, *Die Entwicklung der deutschen Volkswirtschaftslehre im neunzehnten Jahrhundert*, II, Leipzig, 1908, ch. 27; F. Zahn (ed.), *Die Statistik in Deutschland nach ihrem heutigen Stand*, Munich, 1911. In the United States, courses were offered in sixteen universities and colleges in the 1890's, principally by economists (among them I. Fisher, H. L. Moore, R. P. Falkner, D. R. Dewey, Walter Willcox), but in most of them the approach was that exemplified in Mayo-Smith's work. Already in the 1880's five institutions were offering courses, and in the 1870's or earlier, several, but little attention was given to tools. See P. J. Fitzpatrick, "The Early Teaching of Statistics in American Colleges and Universities," *American Statistician*, IX (5), 1955, 12–18; also his paper cited in note 12. See also Walker, *op. cit.*, ch. 7.

73. See, e.g., W. C. Mitchell, "Quantitative Analysis in Economic Theory," *American Economic Review*, XV (1925), 1–12; G. Cassel, *On Quantitative Thinking in Economics*, Oxford, 1935, esp. the preface, in which the "reconstruction of economics as a quantitative science" was declared "long overdue." See also opinions expressed in *Econometrica*, I (1932).

74. See Westergaard, *op. cit.*, chs. 4–6; also Phyllis Deane, "The Implications of Early National Income Estimates for the Measurement of Long-Term Economic Growth in the United Kingdom," *Economic Development and Cultural Change*, IV (1955), 3–38. Westergaard (*op. cit.*, pp. 16 ff.) describes London, where John Graunt (1620–74), the father of Demography, lived, as the "cradle of political arithmetic." The term, however, appears to have been first used by Sir William Petty (1623–87) to embrace both "some Mathematicks" and "variety of Matter, Data and Phaenomena, whereupon to exercise the same." See C. H. Hull, *The Economic Writings of Sir William Petty*, Cambridge, 1899, pp. 238–239 *n.* His *Political Arithmetick*, published in 1690, purported to deal with land value, people, building, husbandry, manufactures, commerce, fishery, artisans, interest, taxes, and so on. See Hull, *op. cit.*, pp. 645–646, also other titles on pp. 641–646.

75. See Westergaard, *op. cit.*, pp. 25–28, 33–36, 46–48, 95–96, 129–34; Meitzen, *op. cit.*, pp. 33 ff.; John, *op. cit.*, pp. 155–281; Walker, *op. cit.*, pp. 28–30, 36–37. As early as 1776 "there was published a list of sixty-two titles" dealing with the application of probability to mortality tables and the computation of annuities. See *ibid.*, p. 30. On the subsequent development of life tables and their application to economics, accounting, and other problems, see L. I. Dublin *et al.*, *Length of Life*, New York, 1936, 1949, *passim* and references.

76. See W. F. Willcox's introduction to *Natural and Political Observations Made upon the Bills of Mortality by John Graunt* (1662), Baltimore, 1939, p. xiii. That the supposed orderliness of vital statistical phenomena reflected an

underlying divine order, a common belief in the eighteenth century, is evident in *Die göttliche Ordnung* (1741 ff.) of J. P. Süssmilch, who, after reading W. Derham's *Physico-Theology* (1713), studied Graunt and Petty. "The advance from Süssmilch to Quételet," wrote F. S. Crum, "is the advance from a theological, teleological to a mathematical, physical conception of the uniformities to law of social life." See his "The Statistical Work of Süssmilch," *PASA*, VII (1900–1), 363. See also Westergaard, *op. cit.*, ch. 6; John, *op. cit.*, pp. 241–273; Hull, *op. cit.*, pp. lxxv-lxxix; and note 77.

77. Belief in an underlying order of nature, in part an outgrowth of ancient Greek concern with what endures beneath that which changes, was strong in Newton's time. See A. N. Whitehead, *Science and the Modern World*, New York, 1925, pp. 5–8, 16–21, 27, 90, 134; R. G. Collingwood, *The Idea of Nature*, Oxford, 1945; A. C. Crombie, *Augustine to Galileo*, Cambridge, 1953, *passim;* A. R. Hall, *The Scientific Revolution 1500–1800*, London, 1954, ch. 9; E. Cassirer, *Determinism and Indeterminism in Modern Physics*, New Haven, Conn., 1956, chs. 1–2, 6, 11. Those who dealt with change felt impelled therefore to make its impact compatible with belief in order. Thus Demoivre, discoverer of the normal curve, asserted that, "although Chance produces irregularities," in time "those Irregularities will bear no proportion to the recurrency of that Order which naturally results from Original Design." He thus "expanded the Newtonian theology," said K. Pearson, "and directed statistics into the channel down which it flowed for nearly a century." See Walker, *op. cit.*, pp. 17, 18; also p. 9, on the similar views of J. Bernoulli. Given sufficient knowledge of the state of the universe at a given instant in time, asserted Laplace in 1795 and J. S. Mill a half century later, one could predict its future history. See Laplace, *Philosophical Essay on Probabilities* (Dover), New York, 1951, ch. 2; Mill, *System of Logic* (1843), 6th ed., London, 1865, Bk. III, ch. 5, sec. 7. Neither author supposed, however, that such sufficiency of knowledge would ever be approximated. Seventy years later, K. Pearson was to emphasize that the universe of phenomena was shot through with variation, contingency, and correlation rather than causation. See *The Grammar of Science*, 3d ed., London, 1911, ch. 5. Concerning recent thought, with which this paper does not deal, see H. A. Simon, *Models of Man*, New York, 1957, Pt. I; H. Wold, "Causality and Econometrics," *Econometrica*, XXII (1954), 162–177.

78. Hull, *op. cit.*, pp. lxi–lxxiv, 129, 244, 558 ff. Neither Bacon, nor Petty's friend, Hobbes, used quantitative data in his social science writings.

79. *Ibid.*, pp. 286–287, 256.

80. *Ibid.*, pp. 105–110, 112 ff. Some of these estimates entailed capitalization of prospective income (*ibid.*, pp. 45, 108), aggregating dissimilar forms of wealth, etc. Later writers greatly improved methods for computing present values of future sums. See Westergaard, *op. cit.*, pp. 46 ff., 95.

81. Hull, *op. cit.*, pp. 42–43, 181–183.

82. *Ibid.*, pp. lx–lxi.

83. Both W. S. Jevons (*The Theory of Political Economy*, London, 1871,

pp. 151–153) and G. U. Yule ("Crop Production and Prices: A Note on Gregory King's Law," *JRSS*, LXXVIII [1915], 296–298) fitted equations of demand to "Gregory King's Law." P. H. Wicksteed (in 1889) criticized Jevons' curve and discussed the probable character of a suitable curve (*The Common Sense of Political Economy*, II, ed. L. Robbins, London, 1933, pp. 734–754). The authorship of this law remains in doubt, having first appeared in a work of Charles Davenant, who, in and after 1698, made considerable use of King's materials. See Davenant, *Political and Commercial Works* (collected and revised by Sir Charles Whitworth, London, 1771), II, p. 224; and G. E. Barnett's introduction to *Two Tracts by Gregory King*, Baltimore, 1936, pp. 5–7. Davenant, states Deane (*op. cit.*, p. 12), "produced no research results of his own." Yule, in the paper cited, inquires into how King may have arrived at his "law," which assumes greater price variation than would be expected today. Paul Studenski deals with the early income estimates and the materials on which they are based in *The Income of Nations*, New York, 1958.

84. See Davenant's essay on the balance of trade in *Works*, II. Elsewhere in this volume, and in Volumes I and V, considerable numerical data are presented respecting foreign trade, its profit to England, types of production, and public payments. Income estimates for France, England and Holland, together with other quantitative data, are included in *Two Manuscripts by Charles Davenant*, hitherto unpublished, ed. G. H. Evans, Jr., Baltimore, 1942. It is not clear how many of these data came from King. His *Natural and Political Observations* were first printed in full by George Chalmers, as an appendix to his *Estimate of the Comparative Strength of Great Britain* (1802).

85. Deane, *op. cit.*, p. 12. D. V. Glass describes King's population estimate as "a remarkable effort," in "Gregory King's Estimate of the Population of England and Wales, 1695," *Population Studies*, III (1950), 370.

86. Phyllis Deane, "The Industrial Revolution and Economic Growth: The Evidence of Early British National Income Estimates," *Economic Development and Cultural Change*, V (1957), 159–174.

87. See Deane, *ibid.*; "The Implications . . .;" and "Contemporary Estimates of National Income in the First Half of the Nineteenth Century," *Economic History Review*, VIII (1956), 339–354. See also P. Mathias' comparison of King's and Massie's data (for 1759–60), in "The Social Structure in the Eighteenth Century: A Calculation by Joseph Massie," *Economic History Review*, X (1957), 30–45; and essays on various countries, in Koren, *op. cit.* For descriptions and résumés of pre-1800 and nineteenth-century income estimates, see Paul Studenski, *The Income of Nations*, New York, 1958, Pt. 1.

88. See papers by F. Perroux *et al.* in *Income and Wealth*, Series III (ed. M. Gilbert, London, 1953), esp. pp. 53–60, and Series V (ed. S. Kuznets, London, 1955), pp. 49 ff. A. L. Lavoisier's estimate, based partly upon physiocratic principles, *De la richesse territoriale du royaume de France* (included in E. Daire and G. de Molinari, eds., *Mélanges d'économie politique*, I, Paris, 1847, pp. 575–601), appeared in 1791. J. L. Lagrande's *Essai d'arithmétique*

politique (in Daire and De Molinari, *op. cit.*, pp. 608–614), devoted to an estimate of "les premiers besoins de l'intérieur de la république," appeared in 1796. Fifteenth-century incomes for Bâle, Frankfort, and Augsburg apparently were not worked over until G. Schmoller used them (see note 63 above).

89. Estimates for the nineteenth and twentieth centuries for countries for which national income data are available are reported in S. Kuznets' "Quantitative Aspects of the Economic Growth of Nations," which appeared as two appendices to *Economic Development and Cultural Change,* V (1956–57), and in Colin Clark, *Conditions of Economic Progress,* London, 1940, 1957. See also Studenski, *op. cit.*

90. The first writer on economics to make use of graphical representation was Nicole Oresme (c. 1320–82); and this was four centuries after the first known graph had been published. See H. G. Funkhouser, "A Note on a Tenth-Century Graph," *Osiris,* I (1936), 260–262, and "Historical Development . . .," pp. 269–404. But Oresme did not use such representation in his discussion of economic questions, perhaps because he lacked data. See *ibid.*, pp. 274–277; E. Bridrey, *La théorie de la monnaie au XIV*[e] *siècle: Nicole Oresme,* Paris, 1906.

91. Funkhouser, "Historical Development . . .," p. 280; also H. G. Funkhouser and H. M. Walker, "Playfair and His Charts," *Economic History,* III (1935), 103–109.

92. See, e.g., *An Inquiry into the Permanent Causes of the Decline and Fall of Powerful and Wealthy Nations,* London, 1805; *The Statistical Breviary,* London, 1786. In several of his works Playfair describes himself as the "inventor of Lineal Arithmethic," or graphic method.

93. Funkhouser, "Historical Development . . .," pp. 293–295, 329 ff. The period 1860–1900 is called "the age of enthusiasm in graphics" (*ibid.*, p. 329). Price movements were charted by L. Cook (1828, 1844). J. B. Fourier used a cumulative frequency curve (later called "ogive" by F. Galton) in 1821, but it was not applied to economic data. See *ibid.*, pp. 293, 296–297, 345–346; also 298–299, on Quételet's use of the graphic method; also pp. 299–310, on the early use of illustrated maps and cartograms, which, however, were not often adapted to economic matter. Thomas De Quincey used two diagrams in his discussion of rent. See his *Logic of Political Economy,* London, 1844, ch. 4, sec. 3; see also ch. 1, sec. 2. L. S. Cagnazzi (1769–1852) is reported as being an early user of parallel curves, in Palgrave's *Dictionary of Political Economy,* I, p. 200.

94. Had N. Barbon, D. North, or D. Hume published a large work on political economy, or had R. Cantillon's work appeared when written, any one of these writers might have circumscribed political economy and given it a comparatively stable structure. Both Quesnay and Smith defined economics more widely than many present-day economists would define it.

95. It is not possible here to develop this statement, nor is agreement concerning its specific content ever likely. But see O. H. Taylor, *Economics and Liberalism,* Cambridge, 1955, chs. 2–3 and pp. 149 ff., and H. J. Bittermann's

"Adam Smith's Empiricism and the Law of Nature," *Journal of Political Economy,* XLVIII (1940), 487–520, 703–734.

96. Two of these articles, "Fermiers" and "Grains," which appeared in 1756 and 1757, respectively, are included in A. Oncken's *Oeuvres économiques et philosophiques de F. Quesnay,* Frankfort and Paris, 1888, pp. 159–249. The third, "Hommes," concerned with France's population, was not finally submitted for publication in the *Encyclopédie;* it was first printed in 1908 in the *Revue d'histoire des doctrines économiques et sociales,* I, pp. 3–88. Quesnay's work is now available in A. Sauvy (ed.), *François Quesnay et la Physiocratie,* Paris, 1958.

97. See Oncken, *op. cit.,* pp. 164–165, 171 ff., 177–179, 184–186.

98. *Ibid.,* pp. 197, 210–211. Prices, quantities, total revenue, expenses, and profits are tabulated for years ranging from "abondante" to "mauvaise," and averaged. Quesnay presents what amounts to a demand schedule, but it is not Marshallian since the data, from different years, are not explicitly subjected to a *ceteris paribus* condition.

99. *Ibid.,* pp. 197–214. See also pp. 221–223, 225–226.

100. He gives wheat prices in terms both of money at the time a price was recorded and of money in his own times. Some of his prices are taken from Bishop Fleetwood's *Chronicon Preciosum* (1707), in which it is estimated that a fellowship-holder's support which had cost £5 in 1400 cost £30 in 1707. This is perhaps the earliest fairly careful attempt to measure changes in the value of money over long periods. See E. Cannan, *A Review of Economic Theory,* London, 1930, p. 160. Smith's tables appear at the close of Book I of his *Wealth of Nations* (Modern Library issue of E. Cannan's edition), pp. 251–258. See also Ernest Rubin, "Statistics and Adam Smith," *American Statistician,* XIII (2), 1959, 23–24.

101. See e.g., *Wealth of Nations,* pp. 5 ff., 18 ff., 34 ff., 43, 48, 68, 75 ff., 84, 89 ff., 103, 109, 148–152, 167–170, 244–246, 277, 280–281, 286, 298 ff., 302–304, 318, 337, 340, 345, 349, 444, 448–455, 462–463, 468, 475, 485–487, 502–505, 517–520, 567–570, 610–611, 656–657, 684, 700–703, 705, 708–711, 770, 772, 774, 788–789, 833, 840–841, 855, 865–902. Smith cited King and Davenant several times (*ibid.,* pp. 77, 196, 280) but had "no great faith in political arithmetic" (*ibid.,* p. 501).

102. Smith believed that the quantity of labor commanded by a commodity "from century to century and from year to year" afforded the best measure of its "real value" and of variations therein. "From century to century, corn is a better measure than silver, because from century to century, equal quantities of corn will command the same quantity of labour more nearly than equal quantities of silver. From year to year, on the contrary, silver is a better measure than corn, because equal quantities of it will more nearly command the same quantity of labour." See *ibid.,* pp. 36–37, also 35, 74–75, 85–86, 476–477. In a long digression (*ibid.,* pp. 176–242), he deals with variations in the value of silver between 1350 and the 1770's, expressing its value in terms of wheat, contrasting its value with that of gold, and inquiring

into the circumstances that affect the values of silver and of commodities. Rubin (*op. cit.*, p. 24) describes Smith's tabular presentation as "remarkable" and his interpretations as "illuminating."

103. E.g., see *Wealth of Nations*, pp. 64 ff., 277 ff., 294, 335, 793, 816. In *The Theory of Moral Sentiments* (Bohn's Standard Library, London, 1853, pp. 425–426) he suggested that a doctrine, if too systematized, lost some of its usefulness. He did not see fit to quantify his discussion of utility, as had Bernoulli. In a discussion of astronomy (*The Essays of Adam Smith*, London, 1872, pp. 352, 384) Smith described an explanatory system as "an imaginary machine invented to connect together in the fancy those different movements and effects which are already in reality performed," but he made its continued acceptance depend upon its consonance with observation, its capacity to connect observations, and its comparative simplicity. W. O. Thweatt has made a quantitative translation of one of Smith's models, in "A Diagrammatic Presentation of Adam Smith's Growth Model (Note)," *Social Research*, XXIV (1957), 227–230.

104. G. Weulersse once commented on the "mathematical demon by which the physiocrats in a way were possessed." See his *Le mouvement physiocratique en France* (*de 1756 à 1770*), II, Paris, 1910, p. 125.

105. See Oncken, *op. cit.*, pp. 104, 305–328, 494–515, 696–718. See also Marquis de Mirabeau, *Philosophie rurale ou économie générale et politique de l'agriculture*, Amsterdam, 1763; N. Baudeau, *Explication du tableau économique*, 1770 (included in E. Daire [ed.], *Physiocrates*, Paris, 1846). The dimensions employed in Quesnay's abbreviated table are somewhat in keeping with those found in "Grains." Quesnay's earliest (1758) table merely represented the activities of an individual farmer; these could, however, be transformed into national terms.

106. See A. Phillips, "The Tableau Économique as a Simple Leontief Model," *Quarterly Journal of Economics*, LXIX (1955), 137–144. See also my "The Physiocrats and Say's Law of Markets," *Journal of Political Economy*, LIII (1945), 196–205; R. Suaudreau, *Les représentations figurées des physiocrates, Paris*, 1947; also Sauvy, *op. cit.*, Vol. I.

107. The correspondence incorporating Du Pont's report of his lost original paper was published in 1892, but its editor, the historical-school economist Karl Knies, considered the price-curve diagram too "inconsequential" to be included in this correspondence. The diagram first appears in Pierre Samuel Du Pont de Nemours, *On Economic Curves*, ed. with introduction by H. W. Spiegel, Baltimore, 1955.

108. "Many of the questions both in morals and politics seem to be of the nature of problems de maximus and minimus in Fluxions; in which there is always a point where a certain effect is greatest, while on the other side of this point it gradually diminishes." See his *Observations on the Effects of the Corn Laws* (1814), ed. J. H. Hollander, Baltimore, 1932, p. 25. See also Ernest Rubin, "The Quantitative Data and Methods of the Rev. T. R. Malthus," *The American Statistician*, XIV (1960), 3–12.

109. Concerning the period 1790–1870, during which there was progress in social statistics but very little in economic statistics, Schumpeter writes: "The statistician's pure theory and the economist's pure theory were almost completely divorced;" and he adds that they were to "remain divorced until our own day." See *History*, p. 525. The last statement underestimates the degree of rapprochement already achieved between 1880 and 1917. The role of methodology in various of the post-1870 schools is competently dealt with by T. W. Hutchison, in *A Review of Economic Doctrines, 1870–1929*, Oxford, 1953.

110. See, e.g., John Barton, *Conditions of the Labouring Classes of Society* (1817), Baltimore, 1934, p. 45. Malthus (treated in the section above) was essentially a member of the classical school, even with respect to methodology. Concerning contemporary criticisms of his views see, e.g., Kenneth Smith, *The Malthusian Controversy*, London, 1915, and H. A. Bonner, *Hungry Generations*, New York, 1955. A modified position respecting the "principle of population" was taken even by some members of the classical school. See my "Marshall on the Population Question," *Population Studies*, VIII (1955), 265–668; M. Blaug, "The Empirical Content of Ricardian Economics," *Journal of Political Economy*, LXIV (1956), 41–58, esp. 44–49.

111. In his inaugural lecture (1885) upon succeeding Mill's disciple, Henry Fawcett, A. Marshall criticized the classical economists principally on the ground that they had emphasized man's constancy and had neglected that "man himself is in a great measure a creature of circumstances and changes with them" (*Memorials*, p. 153). Malthus had emphasized the variability of man (in *Principles of Political Economy*, 1836, Introduction [written in 1819], p. 1), but he did not differ greatly from other classical economists in the premises from which he reasoned.

112. This remark is applicable even to such accounts as F. S. C. Northrop's (*The Logic of the Sciences and Humanities*, New York, 1947, p. 107 and ch. 13) respecting the nonempirical character of Austrian and classical economics.

113. See Blaug, *op. cit.*, pp. 47, 51. McCulloch's *Statistical Account of the British Empire* appeared in 1837, five years after his statistical *Dictionary, Practical, Theoretical, and Historical of Commerce and Commercial Navigation.* G. R. Porter's *Progress of the Nation*, the first serious statistical account of the British economy (according to Blaug, *op. cit.*, p. 50), appeared initially in 1836–38. Regarding the statistical studies of H. F. von Storch and other contemporaries of the classical economists, see Schumpeter, *History*, pp. 502–503, 511–524.

114. McCulloch, James Mill, and Robert Torrens (see L. Robbins, *Robert Torrens and the Evolution of Classical Economics*, London, 1958, esp. pp. 320–322) were methodological disciples of Ricardo.

115. See W. Bagehot, *Works*, V, Hartford, 1889, p. 402.

116. See letter to Malthus, May 4, 1820, in *The Works and Correspondence of David Ricardo*, ed. P. Sraffa, VIII, Cambridge, 1952, p. 184. Ricardo's approach is best illustrated in his *Principles of Political Economy*, in *Works*,

I, 1951. Marshall considered Ricardo's highly abstract bent of mind unique among British economists. See *Memorials,* p. 153; also *Principles of Economics* (1890), 8th ed., London, 1920, p. 761 *n.*

117. See *Works,* III–V. On Ricardo's approach see M. Blaug, *Ricardian Economics,* New Haven, 1958, esp. pp. 31–33. Blaug (*ibid.,* p. 54) endorses J. Viner's view (*Studies in the Theory of International Trade,* New York, 1937, pp. 312–315) that Ricardo did not believe changes in price levels to be measurable by "means of statistical averages" or indices.

118. *Traité d'économie politique,* preliminary discourse. I have used C. R. Prinseps' translation of the fourth French edition, published with notes by C. C. Biddle, in Philadelphia, 1841. The quotation is from p. xix. A. Smith's work, Say believed, was an ingenious but unmethodical assemblance of principles and statistics (*ibid.,* p. xix). In his *Cours complet d'économie politique* (II, Paris, 1840, Pt. IX. pp. 483–507), Say treats statistics much as in the *Traité.* See also "De l'objet et de l'utilité des statistiques," *Revue encyclopédique,* XXXV (1827), 529–553.

119. *Traité,* pp. xxi–xxvi.

120. *Ibid.,* pp. xxvi–xxviii. Say expressed himself with little exactness at times, as when he said, "The rise of price is in direct ratio to the demand, and inverse ratio to the supply" (*ibid.,* p. 290).

121. *Ibid.,* p. xlvii.

122. Senior wrote to Quételet that he did "not consider the truths of political economy as founded on statistical facts, yet its illustrations generally are." See S. L. Levy (ed.), *Industrial Efficiency and Social Economy,* by Nassau W. Senior, I, New York, 1928, p. 60. See also pp. 13–14, where statistics are said to be useful to statesmen, employers of capital, etc., and to show that "the human will obeys laws nearly as certain as those which regulate matter." Senior's views on method in economic science and art is discussed on pages 14–44.

123. See, on Senior's views concerning method, Marian Bowley, *Nassau Senior and Economics* (1937), New York, 1949, ch. 1, esp. pp. 43–44, 49–52, 57–59. Senior rejected Mill's exclusive reliance upon man's supposed desire for wealth, preferring rather to reason in terms of economic-behavioral tendencies (see *ibid.,* pp. 61–64). Although Senior believed reasoning from "hypothetical premises" often produced erroneous conclusions, he described the use of "hypothetical examples" as making for expositive rigor (see Levy, *op. cit.,* I, p. 19).

124. *Essays on Some Unsettled Questions of Political Economy,* London, 1844, pp. 137–138, 152–153; the above was originally written in 1836. See also *A System of Logic* (1843), 6th ed., II, London, 1864, Bk. VI, ch. 9, on the "physical, or concrete deductive method," esp. sec. 3, this being the method referred to in the text. The nonadaptability of the inductive, or "experimental" method, when, as in social science, causes were plural and effects intermixed, is indicated in Bk. III, ch. 10, and Bk. VI, ch. 7; and that of the "geometrical, or abstract method," which treats a social phenomenon as the effect of only

one force instead of as a resultant of several (sometimes conflicting) forces, in Bk. VI, ch. 8. The "concrete deductive" method is intended for a social science in which, of the causes that act jointly, some preponderate. For a critique of Mill's use of deduction see R. P. Anschutz, *The Philosophy of J. S. Mill,* Oxford, 1953, pp. 90 ff., 116 ff.

125. See *Essays,* pp. 148–151; *A System of Logic,* Bk. VI, ch. 9, secs. 3–4. "The Truths of political economy are truths only in the rough." See *Principles of Political Economy* (1st ed., 1848), ed. W. J. Ashley, London, 1921, p. 428. See also my essay on Mill in B. F. Hoselitz (ed.), *Theories of Economic Growth,* Glencoe, Ill., 1960.

126. *A System of Logic,* Bk. VI, ch. 9, secs. 4–6 and ch. 10, secs. 1–3; also ch. 3, sec. 2 and ch. 5, secs. 1–2. Mill's deductive approach thus embraced induction and verification insofar as he deemed them necessary.

127. See *Principles,* esp. Bk. IV, ch. 18; Bk. III; and p. 704. See also Blaug, "The Empirical Content . . .," pp. 54–56. Mill's attitude toward mathematics, about whose use he was at times apprehensive, varied (see Anschutz, *op. cit.,* ch. 9). Mill dealt arithmetically with international trade and elasticity of demand in *Principles,* Bk. III, ch. 18.

128. *The Character and Logical Method of Political Economy* (1857), 2d ed., London, 1875, pp. vi–vii (his italics); also ch. 4–5 on economic laws. Arithmetical illustrations were sometimes used by Cairnes in his other economic writings. Had Cairnes lived later, Persons suggested (*op. cit.,* pp. 262–263), he would have found in multiple and partial correlation a means of eliminating "disturbing causes."

129. *The Character . . .,* pp. 110–117, where he denied that a demand schedule of the sort attributed to Gregory King would stay put through time; he cited T. Tooke in support of this view. A. Comte's denial (see *Philosophie positive,* IV, pp. 512–513) of the applicability of mathematical methods in the social sciences is cited on p. 112.

130. Cairnes, *op. cit.,* pp. 82–85; see also 63–64, 67–68. Other economists, notes Cairnes (*ibid.,* pp. 87–92), have used the method he prescribes.

131. *Ibid.,* pp. 85–87.

132. *Ibid.,* p. 5.

133. See *ibid.,* pp. 34–39, 79–80, 172–175.

134. "The Empirical Content . . .," p. 57.

135. These essays are included in *Essays in Political Economy,* London, 1877.

136. See W. C. Mitchell, *The Backward Art of Spending Money,* New York, 1949, p. 254; Schumpeter, *History,* p. 1089; O. Weinberger, *Mathematische Volkswirtschaftslehre,* Leipzig, 1930, p. 117. See also L. von Mises, *The Theory of Money and Credit* (1912), London, 1934, Pt. II, ch. 5; F. A. Hayek, *The Counter-Revolution of Science,* Glencoe, Ill., 1952, pp. 53, 214, and ch. 3.

137. See J. Viner, "The Utility Theory and Its Critics," *Journal of Political Economy,* XXXIII (1925), 369–387; G. J. Stigler, "The Development of

Utility Theory," *Journal of Political Economy,* LVIII (1950), 307–327, 373–396. Those of the early writers on utility who dealt with it quantitatively are discussed in the section on the mathematical school, below.

138. See H. H. Gossen, *Entwicklung der Gesetze des menschlichen Verkehrs* (1854), 3d ed., Berlin, 1927. Gossen depends largely upon the use of curves, as, later (1889), did the Italian, M. Pantaleoni (*Pure Economics,* London, 1898), in his exposition of utility and related theory. Gossen's work was not known to the three founders of utility economics (i.e., Menger, Jevons, A. Walras) at the time they formulated their initial presentations. According to F. A. Hayek ("Carl Menger," *Economica,* I [1934], 396), F. A. Lange's *Arbeiterfrage* (2d ed., 1870) was the first book to do "justice at all to Gossen's work."

139. See Menger, *Principles of Economics* (tr. from the first edition of *Grundsätze der Volkswirtschaftslehre,* 1871, by J. Dingwall and B. F. Hoselitz), Preface, pp. 67 on time, 114 ff. on value, and 183–186 and ch. 5 on arithmetical models.

140. Hayek ("Carl Menger," pp. 396–397) has found no evidence of Menger's opinion of mathematical methods. Because their methods were nonmathematical, stated F. Y. Edgeworth, the Austrians tended to underrate the role of cost. See *Papers Relating to Political Economy,* II, London, 1925, pp. 277 ff.

141. It was the function of historical statistics (which were to be distinguished from the results of mass observations) to represent systematically the variable factors that produce change, and of history to describe this change. Theoretical analysis of statistical materials might yield laws relating to the coexistence and the sequence of social phenomena. See *Untersuchungen über die Methode der Socialwissenschaften und der politischen Oekonomie insbesondere* (Leipzig, 1883), No. 18 in the Series of Reprints of Scarce Tracts in Economics and Political Science, London, 1933, pp. 6, 8–9. See also *Die Irrthümer des Historismus,* Vienna, 1884, sixth letter, in which economic history and statistics are described as tools or auxiliary sciences on which theoretical economics may draw. See also A. W. Small, *Origins of Sociology,* Chicago, 1924, chs. 11, 14; and G. Ritzel, *Schmoller versus Menger,* Frankfurt am Main, 1950, esp. pp. 68–86.

142. Menger's approach to economics became influential in many countries, though less so in Germany (because of opposition of the later historical school) than elsewhere. See Hayek, "Carl Menger," pp. 407–411. Menger's approach is continued most effectively today by L. von Mises. See, e.g., his *Theory and History,* New Haven, 1957, pp. 89–90, 260, where "in the field of human action" statistics is said to be, not a method of inductive research, but one of "historical research," and where the events dealt with by the "historical sciences of human action" cannot be interpreted as a manifestation of a "general law." The econometrician is similarly hampered by the inconstancy of the economic behavior with which he proposes to deal (*ibid.,* pp. 10–12). On the persistence of anti-empiricism in the Austrian school see A. R. Sweezy, "The Interpretation

of Subjective Value Theory in the Writings of the Austrian Economists," *Review of Economic Studies,* I (1934), 176–185. Limitations upon the applicability of the methods of natural science, already noted by Mill and stressed by the Austrians, are dealt with in Hayek's *Counter-Revolution of Science.*

143. See *The Positive Theory of Capital* (1888), trans. W. Smart, New York, 1923, Preface. This is the second volume of *Kapital und Kapitalzins,* of which the first appeared in 1884; new three-volume editions appeared in 1909–14 and in 1921 (of this last, an English translation, *Capital and Interest,* South Holland, Ill., 1959, has just appeared). See also "The Historical *vs.* the Deductive Method in Political Economy," *Annals of the American Academy of Political and Social Science,* I (1890), 244–271, and "The Austrian Economists," *ibid.,* 361–384. Scaling is touched upon in a discussion of "the measurability of sensations" in *Capital and Interest,* III, ch. 10.

144. *Natural Value* (1888), trans. C. A. Malloch, London, 1893, Preface and ch. 1.

145. *Ibid.,* p. 88; see also, G. J. Stigler, *Production and Distribution Theories,* New York, 1941, pp. 163–171.

146. *Social Economics* (1914), trans. A. F. Hinrichs, New York, 1927, Preface and pp. 3–13. Mathematical means have "justified" no "great truth" or application of economic theory (*ibid.,* p. 13).

147. It is somewhat misleading to speak of a mathematical school, as the term is used here. For, whereas each other school embraces only persons who carried on economic analysis in a similar systematic way, the mathematical school embraces all (except those treated elsewhere) who made use of mathematics in economic analysis.

148. See, e.g., F. C. Mills, "On Measurement in Economics," in R. G. Tugwell (ed.), *The Trend of Economics,* New York, 1924, pp. 37–46, and the works cited.

149. Reference may be made also to *Economic and Industrial Delusions* (New York, 1891, ch. 3), in which A. B. and H. Farquhar employ charts and tabular data to show that increases in import duties by the United States made exports less than they otherwise would have been. What amounts to a verbal regression equation appears on pages 74–75.

150. "*Economic laws,* or statements of economic tendencies, are those social laws which related to branches of conduct in which the strength of the motives chiefly concerned can be measured by a money price" (See *Principles,* p. 33). On the measurability of motives, see pp. 14–28, 782–783; on economic laws, pp. 29–37; on methods in economics, pp. 770–784. See also *Memorials,* pp. 152–187, 421 ff.

151. *Memorials,* pp. 162–167, 309–310; *Principles,* pp. 773–774. Marshall seems to have recognized that without the guidance of economic models one could not get answers to economic questions through the use of statistics or mathematics; this was the classical view also.

152. *Ibid.,* pp. 459 *n.,* 765–766, 771–775, 781 ff. Marshall looked upon economics as a "branch of biology broadly interpreted," in that each dealt with

"a matter, of which the inner nature and constitution, as well as the outer form, are constantly changing" (*ibid.*, p. 772); but he ruled out emergence, saying "economic forces combine mechanically rather than chemically" (*ibid.*, p. 771). Mill discussed the notion of emergence in his *System of Logic,* Bk. III, chs. 6, 10, and Bk. VI, ch. 7.

153. *Principles,* pp. 781–782, also 101, 357; *Memorials,* pp. 97–99. Of Marshall's seven major contributions to economic knowledge (according to J. M. Keynes), five rest upon or incorporate reasoning of a mathematical sort (see *ibid.*, pp. 41–48).

154. See, e.g., *Principles,* prefaces to 1st and 8th editions; *Memorials,* pp. 419–421, 427–429. Marshall had been influenced by Cournot and Von Thünen.

155. See paper cited in note 44 above, in which, besides defining elasticity of demand for the first time, he proposed grouping *historical* curves in order that correlations might be discerned and suggested a device for disclosing proportional rates of change in quantities represented by historical curves (see *Memorials,* pp. 175–187, 501).

156. *Ibid.*, pp. 188–211, also 31–33; *Money Credit & Commerce,* London, 1923, Bk. I, chs. 2–3 and Appendix B.

157. *The Scope and Method of Political Economy,* p. 30. He distinguished, as had Senior, Mill, and others, between economics as an art and economics as a positive science (*ibid.*, pp. 34–35).

158. *Ibid.*, pp. 85, 101, 296–314. Illustrative of universal principles were variation in utility, preference of greater to lesser gain, law of rent (*ibid.*, pp. 310–314).

159. *Ibid.*, pp. 254, 260, 266–267. "It would be difficult to exaggerate the gain that has resulted from the application of mathematical ideas to the central problems of economic theory" (*ibid.*, p. 267).

160. *Ibid.*, pp. 343–344.

161. *Ibid.*, p. 344.

162. *Ibid.*, pp. 351–370.

163. *Ibid.*, pp. 320–327. Keynes does not specifically discuss the role of statistics in economic history. He did not consider economics "an essentially historical science" (*ibid.*, p. 314).

164. Bowley lists 74 books and papers and a number of reviews. See *Edgeworth's Contributions,* pp. 129–139; also J. M. Keynes, "Francis Ysidro Edgeworth," in *Essays in Biography,* London, 1933.

165. Bowley, *Edgeworth's Contributions,* p. 2; also p. 92 on his neglect of the problem that arises when frequency distributions based on random samples differ. His important work on index numbers represented a partial exception to the statement in the text, however. See *Papers Relating to Political Economy* (3 vols.), I, London, 1925, pp. 195–405. Included here are Edgeworth's articles and reviews which appeared in the *Economic Journal,* 1891–1921.

166. "On Methods of Statistics," p. 194; also pp. 211–212, on the application of statistics to the study of poetry. Edgeworth sometimes made use of

inverse probability and appeal to equality of ignorance (see e.g., Bowley, *Edgeworth's Contributions*, p. 120).

167. "On the Application of Mathematics to Political Economy," in *Papers*, II, pp. 273–312, esp. pp. 274–277. Mathematical analysis yielded conclusions not attainable with nonmathematical methods. See, e.g., *Papers*, I, pp. 143–191; also II, pp. 367–386, on applications of differential calculus, especially in the "more mechanical" sector of political economy. See also *Mathematical Psychics*, London, 1881, in which various applications of mathematics to the "moral sciences" are treated.

168. *Papers*, II, p. 388; in the paper referred to, Edgeworth applies probabilities to a number of problems and contrasts the inexact axioms of economics with the similarly inexact axioms of mathematical physics.

169. *Papers*, II, pp. 290–291; I, p. 139.

170. Bowley, *Edgeworth's Contributions*, pp. 6–9, 118–121. See also, on a priori conditions, *ibid.*, pp. 7 ff., 34–35, and *Papers, passim.*

171. *Ibid.*, pp. 273, 281.

172. See, e.g., *ibid.*, I, p. 11; II, pp. 288, 290.

173. E.g., William Newmarch declared ("The Progress of Economic Science During the Last Thirty Years," *JRSS*, XXIV [1861], 451–467) that economics had ceased to be an abstract science, that conclusions based upon careful observation and investigation of facts had replaced "deductions arrived at by geometrical reasoning," and that its having "become a science almost entirely experimental" was the "most important fact" in the history of economics since 1830. The last two volumes of Thomas Tooke's *History of Prices* (1838–57; republished in 1928 under T. E. Gregory's editorship) were brought out by Newmarch.

174. "Moore's Economic Cycles," *Quarterly Journal of Economics*, XXIX (1914–15), 638. See also H. Schultz, *The Theory and Measurement of Demand*, Chicago, 1938, pp. 51 ff. That a portion of the demand curve for consumers' goods might slope upward was known before 1900. See W. Jaffe's note to his translation of L. Walras, *Elements of Pure Economics*, London, 1954, p. 500.

175. See Young, *op. cit.*, pp. 241–244. Mills's argument appears in "On Measurement . . . ," esp. pp. 46–64. Persons did not approve Mills's view that what principally distinguished economic from physical laws was the degree of scatter of observations about the equations expressing such laws (*op. cit.*, pp. 274–275).

176. See Edgeworth, *Papers*, II, p. 273. Jevons' paper, read in 1862, was printed in the *JRSS*, XXIX (1866), 282–287, to which journal he contributed a number of papers. His bibliography is included in posthumous editions of *The Theory of Political Economy* (1871), ed. H. S. Jevons.

177. See G. H. Bosquet, "Histoire de l'économie mathematique jusq'à Cournot," *Metroeconomica*, X (1958), 121–138; R. M. Robertson, "Mathematical Economics before Cournot," *Journal of Political Economy*, pp. 523–536; H. Reichardt, *Augustin A. Cournot: sein Beitrag zur exakten Wirtschafts-*

wissenschaft, Tübingen, 1954; R. D. Theocharis, "Joseph Lang and Macroeconomics," *Economica,* XXV (1958), 319–325. See also O. Weinberger, *Mathematische Volkswirtschaftslehre,* pp. 31–43; M. Brodsky and P. Rocher, *L'économie politique,* Paris, 1949, pp. 9–15. A not quite complete but still insufficiently selective bibliography of mathematico-economic books is included in Jevons, *The Theory of Political Economy,* 5th ed., New York, 1957, pp. 322–331. If we include also several items mentioned by E. R. A. Seligman (*Essays in Economics,* New York, 1925, pp. 82–83, 128), it is evident that by 1838 about 40 items (by thirty authors) had appeared, of which about half are fairly mathematical. Only three of these authors (Bernoulli, Beccaria, and Isnard) reasoned in an explicitly mathematical manner, Schumpeter has said (*History,* pp. 955–958, particularly 955). I. Fisher's bibliography of mathematical works covers 1711–1897; it is classified. It appears in the N. T. Bacon translation of Cournot's first work—*Researches into the Mathematical Principles of the Theory of Wealth,* New York, 1897, 1929. R. D. Theocharies, *Early Development in Mathematical Economics* (forthcoming) deals with early mathematical economics.

178. See G. J. Stigler, "The Development of Utility Theory," *Journal of Political Economy,* LVIII (1950), 307–327, 373–396, esp. 392–396. Stigler deals with "the probability-less idea of utility," an idea which began to be discredited by Pareto. See L. J. Savage, *The Foundations of Statistics,* New York, 1954, pp. 91–104, esp. 95–97.

179. See Marget, *op. cit.,* I, pp. 10–11; II, pp. 20, 154, 264, 270–271; Schultz, *op. cit.,* pp. 5–6; also M. Fasiani, "Note sui saggi economici di Francesco Fuoco," *Annali de statistica e di economia,* V (1937), 98 ff., 164 ff., 271 ff. Briscoe is mentioned by Schumpeter, *History,* pp. 296, 314–316. F. Hoffmann (*Kritische Dogmengeschichte der Geldwerttheorien,* Leipzig, 1907) undertook to translate into equation form some eighteenth-century verbal formulations. G. Ceva, probably the first mathematical economist and an advocate of the use of rational, mathematical models in economic analysis (*De re nummaria,* etc., 1711), apparently understood the nature of the relationship between money and prices.

180. See Marget, *op. cit.,* I, pp. 10–11; and Robertson, *op. cit.,* p. 534 on Lang, who is not mentioned by Marget.

181. See Marget, *op. cit.,* I, pp. 10–11; II, pp. 56–57; J. Viner, *Studies in the Theory of International Trade,* New York, 1937, pp. 248 ff.; also H. Hegeland, *The Quantity Theory of Money,* Göteberg, 1951, pp. 85–87. T. P. Thompson, the first British writer writer to use calculus in economic analysis, employed it to determine the degree to which a government might derive gain from the systematic issue of irredeemable currency. See Robertson's summary, *op. cit.,* pp. 527–529.

182. See, e.g., Hegeland, *op. cit.,* chs. 4–7, 9–10; also Marget, *op. cit., passim.*

183. My discussion is based generally upon Stigler's "The Development . . . ." See also Robertson's treatment of Bernoulli (*op. cit.,* pp. 524–526) and his

statement that E. Mariotte supposed incremental utility to diminish (*Essai de logique*, Paris, 1678). Graphical analysis was used by Dupuit (see below) and by H. H. Gossen, who also used algebraic analysis. Jevons employed calculus and geometry, as did Walras. The long neglect of Gossen's work is attributable at least in part to his failure as an expositor and to barriers to the diffusion of ideas which existed in greater measure in Germany than in Britain.

184. See Stigler, "The Development . . . ," esp. Pt. II; Schultz, *op. cit.*, chs. 18–19. It was the mathematical economists who sought to distinguish complementary from substitutive goods.

185. Marshall had already developed the concept in his privately circulated *Pure Theory of (Domestic) Values* (1879). Dupuit's papers, a number of which appeared in the *Journal des économistes* between 1849 and 1865, are assembled in M. de Bernardi (ed.), *De l'utilité et de sa mesure*, Torino, 1934. On Cournot, see note 186.

186. See *The Graphic Representation of the Laws of Supply and Demand*, (1887), London, 1931, pp. 107–114. Jenkin used supply and demand curves to explain price behavior and to support the view (of which he was apparently the first English exponent) that trade unions could raise wages (*ibid.*, pp. 76–106), a view shared by other mathematical economists (e.g., P. H. Wicksteed, *The Common Sense of Political Economy*, 1910, Bk. III, ch. 2; Edgeworth, *Mathematical Psychics*, 1881, pp. 43–45, 136 ff.). Unlike Jevons, Jenkin considered utility unmeasurable (*ibid.*, pp. 109–110) and therefore reasoned entirely in terms of supply and demand curves. Although Jevons' account of the advantages of exchange involved reasoning of the sort that underlies some treatments of consumer's surplus, he did not always use the concept, in part because he did not believe it possible always to assess in finite terms what he called "total utility" (see *Theory*, 1st ed., 1871, pp. 54–58, 95 ff.). Cournot seems to have been aware of a kind of consumer's rent, but he did not utilize it, not deeming it measurable (see *Researches*, pp. 133–134, 138, 154; also pp. 8–9, where wealth is defined in terms of exchange value).

187. I have used the French translation, *Recherches sur la théorie de prix*, Paris, 1914. Included are over 84 graphs and 4 mathematical appendices, one devoted to the equations of the graphs. The authors employ total-cost, total-demand, total-revenue, etc. curves. See, e.g., Pt. I, ch. 1 and fig. 5; also Pt. III, ch. 1. For a brief account of the development of the concept of consumer's surplus, see R. W. Houghton, "A Note on the Early History of Consumer's Surplus," *Economica*, XXV (1958), 49–57.

188. See P. H. Wicksteed, *The Common Sense of Political Economy*, Bk. II, ch. 4. Demand was expressed in algebraic forms several times in the eighteenth century. Thus in 1771 P. Verri, postulating what amounts to unitary elasticity of demand or constant outlay, wrote $P = D/S$. P. Frisi wrote (possibly under the influence of Hume's interest analysis) $P = C/V$, where C stands for number of buyers and V for number of sellers. See Robertson, *op. cit.*, pp. 526–527; also Marget, *op. cit.*, II, pp. 264, 271. Verri, of an econometrical turn of mind,

was one of the first "to figure out a balance of payments," Schumpeter reports (*History*, p. 178).

189. *Researches in the Mathematical Principles of the Theory of Wealth* (1838), New York, 1929, esp. chs. 4, 8. In his Foreword (1927), I. Fisher indicated that "mathematical method" had become very "general" during the two decades succeeding 1897. Cournot, having remarked the errors in Canard's work (summarized in M. Brodsky, *L'économie politique mathématique*, Paris, 1949, pp. 9–14) and noted strong opposition to the use of mathematics in economics (which resulted in the complete neglect of his work for nearly forty years), indicated that economic analysis involved the study of magnitudes, functions, etc., to which calculus and mechanics were well adapted (see Preface). Cournot makes use of calculus, geometry, and algebra. Elsewhere, however, observing that *mundum regunt numeri*, he remarked that geometry and mechanics were incapable of adequately explaining man's behavior. It was essential to apply statistical theory—not mere compilations, but rules founded upon probability. Crucial quotations from Cournot's writings on probability are given by Moore in "The Statistical Complement . . . ," pp. 3–5.

190. Hutchison, *op. cit.*, pp. 133 ff., 186 ff.

191. See Cournot, *Researches*, pp. 52–54. On some early notions respecting elasticity of demand, see Marget, *op. cit.*, II, chap. 4, esp. pp. 148–153, 206–210; also Robertson, *op. cit.*, p. 535, on Whewell. Cournot suggested (*op. cit.*, p. 47) that the shape of the demand function may be affected by the distribution of wealth, as also did Dupuit (Houghton, *op. cit.*, p. 50), just as Say and others had implied (Marget, *op. cit.*, pp. 206–209).

192. See Houghton, *op. cit.*, p. 50; Marshall, *Principles*, p. 132; Auspitz and Lieben, *op. cit.*, p. 117.

193. See *Elements of Pure Economics*, trans. W. Jaffe, London, 1954.

194. Schultz, *op. cit.*, pp. 54–58. Schultz indicated that the theory of utility had been useful to the study of demand and remained so (*ibid.*, pp. 54–55; chs. 18–19).

195. Here I draw on G. J. Stigler, "The Early History of Empirical Studies of Consumer Behavior," *Journal of Political Economy*, LXII (1954), 95–113, particularly 103–105. Laspeyres was a strong advocate of the use of statistics in economic analysis (see *Die Kathedersocialisten und die statistischen Congresse*, Berlin, 1875). Living at a time when statisticians emphasized description rather than analysis and explanation, Engel did not venture to translate his findings into terms of income-elasticity of demand.

196. Undoubtedly the work on trend-fitting, the use of moving averages and correlation, the correlation of price series, Norton's getting a supply curve for call loans, etc., helped generate the interest that gave rise to demand-curve estimation (see Stigler, "The Early History . . .," pp. 105–106).

197. See *ibid.*, pp. 106–113; Schultz, *op. cit.*, pp. 63–83, 107 ff., 607–666, and p. 63, where the "statistical study of demand" is described as the "creation of one man," H. L. Moore. On supply functions and elasticity, see H. Schultz, *Statistical Laws of Demand and Supply*, Chicago, 1928; and H. J. Bitterman,

"Elasticity of Supply," *American Economic Review,* XXIV (1934), 417–429. R. Benini, as noted above, seems to have been the first to estimate price elasticity of demand (for coffee). See H. Wold, "Causal Inference from Observational Data," *JRSS* (Ser. A), CXIX (1956), 33.

198. See Stigler, "The Early History . . . ," pp. 95–102. According to H. Wold and L. Jureen (*Demand Analysis,* New York, 1953, p. 328), A. A. Konyus was "the first to introduce income as an explicit variable in demand functions."

199. See H. S. Houthakker, "An International Comparison of Household Expenditure Patterns, Commemorating the Centenary of Engel's Law," *Econometrica,* XXV (1957), 532–551; Zimmerman, *Consumption and Standards of Living,* New York, 1936. Houthakker used a double logarithmic function, much as did Engel in 1857. See also J. Marschak, *Elastizität der Nachfrage,* Tübingen, 1931.

200. Stigler, "The Early History . . . ," pp. 102–103.

201. See G. J. Stigler, "Perfect Competition, Historically Contemplated," *Journal of Political Economy,* LXV (1957), 1–17, esp. 5 ff. Edgeworth (*Mathematical Psychics,* London, 1881, pp. 17–19) was the first to attempt a rigorous definition, Jevons having approximated Cournot, and Walras and Pareto having given little attention to defining competition. Moore listed the supposed hypotheses ("Paradoxes . . . ,"); Marshall was unsystematic. Despite these definitional variations, it is evident that much of the content of any one definition overlapped that of others, with the result that the concept could be and was effectively used, though the conditions of competitive equilibrium were not uniformly defined. The mathematical economists, though favorable to a competitive regime, did not identify competitive equilibrium with what, for a time, was thought of as the satisfaction- or welfare-maximizing equilibrium.

202. Firm-equilibrium conditions under competition were not neglected, of course, being but one case of the set of cases of firm equilibrium. It was, however, the imperfect-competition situation that commanded most interest.

203. See, e.g., Edgeworth's review (*Papers,* III, pp. 136–144) of H. Cunynghame's *A Geometrical Political Economy,* Oxford, 1904. His two Swedish contemporaries, G. Cassel and K. Wicksell, favored symbols over geometry, as did Pareto and Walras. J. M. Keynes described Cunynghame's first paper (see *Economic Journal,* II, [1892] 35 ff.), in which geometrical methods were skilfully used and ably defended, as of "great interest" to students "of the development of graphical methods" ("Obituary: Sir Henry Cunynghame," *Economic Journal,* XLV [1935], 403).

204. Buquoy's concern was with how far plowing should be carried. He made use of continuous functions which could be used to represent demand, cost, supply, etc., though he did not apply them in his algebraic analysis of "natural price" (see Robertson, *op. cit.,* pp. 527, 529–530). He was, in point of time, the third individual to make use of calculus in economic analysis. C. Beccaria in 1765 had used algebra to determine the point of indifference between smuggling (subject to loss through confiscation) and paying duty, but he did not translate this into a supply curve of smuggling service; his exposition

was graphed in 1792 by G. Silio, Beccaria having explained how the graph should be drawn (see Robertson, *op. cit.*, pp. 530–531).

205. *Researches*, chs. 5–7. This last conclusion (*ibid.*, pp. 102–104) ran counter to what economists then supposed, much as did Edgeworth's paradoxical finding (e.g., *Papers*, II, pp. 89–96) that a tax on a monopolist supplying two commodities, demand for which is correlated, may cause the price asked for each to be reduced. Monopoly, in short, presented special problems not to be inferred immediately from the study of competitive situations. Mathematical method was well suited to bring out the differences.

206. See A. H. Leigh, "Von Thünen's Theory of Distribution and the Advent of Marginal Analysis," *Journal of Political Economy*, LIV (1946), 481–502. On the subsequent development of this theory and of its criticism by mathematical economists who stressed the interdependence of prices, see G. J. Stigler, *Production and Distribution Theories*, New York, 1941; also P. H. Douglas, *The Theory of Wages*, New York, 1934, Pt. I, esp. pp. 34–44, on the long-continued neglect of what was significant in Von Thünen's work.

207. See *ibid.*, pp. 37 ff., 203 ff. It was H. L. Moore, however, who, by his inductive study of French wage and output statistics, established a basis for the statistical determination of productions (*ibid.*, pp. 107 ff.). Walras and Pareto dealt with production coefficients in the abstract, but did not undertake to estimate them.

208. Most of the then mathematical economists discussed this question. See Stigler, *Production and Distribution Theories*, ch. 12. See also Wicksteed, *The Co-ordination of the Laws of Distribution*, London, 1894. The issue did not arise so long as one of the factors was treated as a residual claimant (as by Jevons). In 1888 appeared Wicksteed's *The Alphabet of Economic Science*, in which the Jevonian system is expounded graphically and with the aid of calculus.

209. E.g., D. Lardner in 1850 (*Railway Economy*, 1850, cited by Jevons, *Theory*, 1st ed., p. 17) indicated, as had Cournot, that the point of maximum profit coincided with the point where marginal cost and marginal revenue were equal. Lardner's work included a great deal of quantitative data relating to costs, prices, and pricing problems in the railway industry. Edgeworth (*Papers*, I, pp. 64, 71–72) used curves similar to Lardner's total-receipts and total-expenses curves, but indicated the maximum-profit point depended upon whether monopoly or competition obtained. In 1839 Ellet, a civil engineer like Dupuit, used calculus to analyze pricing policies and their effects (see C. D. Calsoyas, "The Mathematical Theory of Monopoly in 1839: Charles Ellet, Jr.," *Journal of Political Economy*, LVIII [1950], 162–170). Jevons expressed great indebtedness to Lardner's work and approach (see R. M. Robertson, "Jevons and His Precursors," *Econometrica*, XIX [1951], pp. 229–249, esp. 240–241). Whewell, J. Tozer, J. Lubbock, F. Jenkin, A. De Morgan, and a number of empirical writers also influenced Jevons (see *ibid*).

210. Regarding the fact that competition and monopoly were the typical cases conceived, see Hutchison, *op. cit.*, pp. 222–223, 307–319. Cf. Edge-

worth, *Papers;* Marshall, *Principles;* Auspitz and Lieben, *op. cit.*, Pt. VI. Walras used a competition model.

211. On Isnard see Robertson, "Mathematical Economics before Cournot," pp. 532–533. See also Cournot, *Researches,* chs. 3, 7; Walras, *Elements;* Jevons, *Theory,* 1st ed., pp. 113 ff.; Cassel, *Nature and Necessity of Interest* and *Theory of Social Economy;* Marshall, *Principles.*

212. See "L'interpolazione per la ricerca delle legge economiche," *Giornale degli Economisti,* XXXIV–XXXV (1907), esp. 336. In this number (pp. 964–992) M. Pantaleoni gives an impression of the increase of quantification in his "Una visione cinemtatografica del progresso della scienza economica, 1870–1907." The words "e Statistica" were added to the title of this journal in 1910. A bibliography of Pareto's writings was published in this journal in 1924 (LXIV, pp. 144–153).

213. J. M. Keynes reviews Jevons' contributions in "William Stanley Jevons, 1835–1882," *JRSS,* XLIX (1936), 516–548. See also P. G. Craigie, "Jevons's Coal Question: Thirty Years After," *JRSS,* LX (1897), 789–810. With Jevons' single-resource approach may be compared V. V. Branford's "On the Calculation of Natural Resources," *JRSS,* LXIV (1901), 380–408. On Moore's contributions see M. Ezekiel, "Moore's Synthetic Economics," *Quarterly Journal of Economics,* XLIV (1930), 663–679; Schultz, *Statistical Laws,* esp. chs. 1, 4, and *The Theory, passim.* See also Moore, *Synthetic Economics,* New York, 1929. On the distinction between statistical and economic questions, a distinction already recognized by the classical school but not adequately clarified until recently, see Wold and Jureen, *op. cit.*

214. Keynes, "William Stanley Jevons . . .," p. 533.

215. *Theory,* pp. 142–155, 191–197. Jevons, besides being a logician, theorist, and empirical philosopher, was, like his great intellectual forebear, Bentham, a social philosopher of nineteenth-century liberal persuasion. See M. R. Konvitz, "An Empirical Theory of the Labor Movement," *Philosophical Review,* LVII (1948), 59–76.

216. One may get an impression of the increasing role of statistical method from *Business Cycles: The Problem and Its Setting,* New York, 1928, by W. C. Mitchell, a leading practitioner. J. P. Norton's work may be looked upon as a way-station from Jevons to Moore. Bowley observed that, except for his use of correlation, unknown to Jevons, Norton's approach was remindful of that of Jevons. See Bowley's review of Norton's *Statistical Studies,* in *Economic Journal,* XII (1902), 516–518. Norton's method was empirical. He established a statistically significant relation between changes in the reserve-deposit ratio and changes in the discount rate. Subsequently, he measured how certain expenses vary with output. See *The Theory of Loan Credit in Relation to Corporation Economics,* in *Publications of the American Economic Association,* Ser. 3, Vol. V, 1904, pp. 278 ff.

217. In the end, of course, the historical approach became merged with others and, early in the present century, the historical school ceased to exist as a recognizable entity. The school had much in common with the American

institutional school which flourished for fifteen or twenty years after World War I and which emphasized quantitative inquiry even more than did the historical school. The institutionalists were not concerned with laws of development, however, and they utilized behavioristic psychology instead of the types implicit in the works of the historical economists. W. Hasbach asserted that economists differed much less in their analyses than controversy over methods implied. See his "Mit welcher Methode wurden die Gesetze der theoretischen Nationaloekonomie gefunden," *Jahrbücher für Nationalökonomie und Statistik,* 3rd ser., XXVII (1904), 289–317; also "Zur Geschichte des Methodenstreites in der politischen Ökonomie," *Jahrbuch für Gesetzgebung, Verwaltung, und Volkswirtschaft,* n.s., XIX (1895), 466–490, 751–808. See also T. Suranyi-Unger, *Economics in the Twentieth Century,* New York, 1931, pp. 45–65, also 35 ff. Boehm-Bawerk noted that Knies, in his later work, made great use of abstract method. See "Historical vs. Deductive Political Economy," p. 259 *n.*

218. See, e.g., H. Grossman, "The Evolutionist Revolt against Classical Economics," *Journal of Political Economy,* LI (1943), 381–396, 506–522; also Hayek, *Counter-Revolution,* pp. 64 ff., 168–207; Schumpeter, *History,* pp. 442 ff., 501 ff., 807 ff.; J. K. Ingram, *A History of Political Economy* (1888), 2d ed., London, 1923, ch. 6.

219. Hayek, *Counter-Revolution,* pp. 196–197, also 168 ff., 175–177, 184–186. Condorcet, a mathematician like Comte and a late eighteenth-century expositor of evolutionism, had favored the application of mathematics to the study of society, as had Bernoulli and others (*ibid.,* pp. 107–108).

220. H. Schumacher even describes their "specific contribution" as "securing recognition for the historical and statistical methods of economic investigation." See his "The Historical School," in *Encyclopaedia of the Social Sciences,* V, New York, 1931, p. 376.

221. J. K. Ingram had less use for statistics than did Ashley. He considered mathematics quite unsuited to economic study and statistics a mere aid to sociology, though one whose importance would increase as that of abstract method declined. See *op. cit.,* pp. 177, 227–228; "Economic Science and Statistics," *JRSS,* XLI (1878), 602–629. W. Cunningham did not make much use of statistics. T. E. C. Leslie, in part a disciple of Comte and an exponent of historical and institutional rather than of abstract economics, looked upon statistical inquiry as complementary to economic analysis. See *Essays in Political and Moral Philosophy,* London, 1879, chs. 10–12, 14–15, 22–26, 29–30. Foxwell (*op. cit.,* pp. 88–90) attributed the transformation of British economics after 1870 to Jevons' work, to the historical approach, and to the rise of humanism. Richard Jones, earliest of the English historical economists and successor to Malthus' chair, helped establish the London Statistical Society. See R. Glenday, "Richard Jones: A Reappraisal," *JRSS,* CXIX, Pt. II (1956), 192–193.

222. See *Die Nationalökonomie der Gegenwart und Zukunft und andere gesammelte Schriften,* with introduction by H. Gehrig, Jena, 1922, ch. 11, pars. 35–53, first published in 1848, and pp. 310–314, on the role of statistics,

published in 1865. Quételet is mentioned (p. 323). I have not seen his *Statistische Mitteilungen über die Volkswirtschaftlichen Kurhessens,* Berlin, 1853.

223. See *Die politische Ökonomie vom Standpunkte der geschichtlichen Methode* (1853), 2d ed., Braunschweig, 1883, pp. 469 ff., 513–516; also 507 ff., on Von Thünen. In *Die Statistik als selbstständige Wissenschaft* he treated Achenwall's "statistics" as history, rejected the Schlözer view that statistics was static history, and, under the influence of Dufau and Quételet, described history as a unique science whose task it was to discover the causal relationships connecting quantifiable facts. See *ibid.,* pp. 65, 68, 112, 115, 167–168, 173–174; also p. 78, where A. F. W. Crome and U. Gobbi are said to have been among the first (along with Playfair) to use charts and diagrams.

224. See *Principles of Political Economy* (tr. J. J. Lalor), I, New York: 1878, secs. 22, 26–29; also *Geschichte der Nationaloekonomik in Deutschland,* Munich, 1874, p. 896, cited by B. Weisz in "Die mathematische Methode in der Nationaloekonomie," *Jahrbücher für Nationalökonomie und Statistik,* XXXI (1878), 313. For a summary of Roscher's historical approach, published in 1843, see W. J. Ashley, "Roscher's Program of 1843," *Quarterly Journal of Economics,* IX (1894), 99 ff.

225. Schmoller's view is thus somewhat remindful of J. S. Mill's. See *Die Volkswirtschaft die Volkswirtschaftslehre, und ihre Methode,* Frankfurt, 1893, pp. 36–37; also *Principes d'économie politique,* I, Paris, 1905, pp. 276 ff. and secs. 42–46, 49–50. His methodological position is treated by Ritzel, *op. cit.,* pp. 48–68, 99 ff.

226. See, e.g., "Die Einkommensverteilung in alter und neurer Zeit," in *Jahrbuch fur Gesetzgebung . . .,* n.s., XIX (1895), 1067–1094, which also appeared in *Bulletin de l'institut de statistique,* IX(2), 1895, 1 ff.; "Die historische Lohnbewegnung von 1300–1900 und ihre Ursachen," *ibid.,* XIV (3), 1905, 223–240. See also *ibid.,* pp. 1–19, for "Statistik des Volks- oder National-einkommens and Vermögens," by A. Wagner, who, though not friendly to the Schmoller school, made use of the historical method. Schmoller (*Principes,* III, p. 482–494) also inferred from a historical study of interest rates that, though they might fall to around 1.5 per cent, capital formation would not fall off. On Schmoller's income study, which appeared shortly after Pareto's, see Bresciani-Turroni, *op. cit.,* note 63 above.

227. Probably representative of the attitudes of later historical economists is J. Conrad's view of statistics as auxiliary to economics and as a means by which systematic and numerical mass observation can be employed to discover interrelations among facts. See *Grundriss zum Studium der politischen Oekonomie* (1915), Pt. I, Jena, 1923, pp. 6–7; also p. 508, on the growing importance of statistics as the state's economic role increases.

228. The data described are found in all three volumes of *Capital.* Marx makes use of a delta occasionally to represent an increment. See *Capital* (published by Charles H. Kerr, Chicago, 1906), I, pp. 168 ff.; III, p. 384. He mentions Quételet and the "law of error" when he is justifying "one day of

average social labour" by supposing the number of workmen concerned to be "large" and "individual differences," to "compensate one another" as do "errors" (*ibid.*, I, pp. 354–355).

229. *Ibid.*, III, pp. 182–203; also 203 ff. See also L. von Bortkiewicz's solution (1907), included in P. M. Sweezy (ed.), *Karl Marx and the Close of His System* (by Boehm-Bawerk), New York, 1949, pp. 199–221; also Sweezy, *The Theory of Capitalist Development*, New York, 1942, ch. 7. Marx, it should be noted, apparently was the first economist to appreciate some of the potentialities present in Quesnay's "tableau économique." Today linear programming and other administrative techniques foreshadowed by marginalist economics are esteemed in the Soviet Union, now a managerial state.

230. See pp. 170, 368, of *Political Economy*, issued by the Institute of Economics of the Academy of Sciences of the U.S.S.R., London, 1957.

231. See *Evolutionary Socialism* (1899), New York, 1911. The data on income changes are reported in ch. 2. See also W. J. Ashley, *Progress of the German Working Class*, London, 1904, pp. 104–114, 140–141.

232. See M. M. Bober, *Karl Marx's Interpretation of History*, Cambridge, 1927, pp. 227–243.

233. Lenin's statistical matter appeared in his writings on imperialism and agriculture and in many of his shorter papers. Lenin would sometimes publish a document including quantitative data under a pseudonym and then cite this source as supporting evidence in papers. On this and other of Lenin's statistical practices see Barbara L. Jones's master's thesis, "Lenin's Use of Statistics," 1954, on deposit at Duke University, Durham, N.C.

234. See Pt. IV of the *General Index* of the *JRSS* (which dealt primarily with Vols. 36–50), pp. 229–247; an author index is included. I have not dealt with vital statistics since they fall largely outside the scope of economics. It was in this sector of applied statistics, however, that the greatest progress was made in the nineteenth century. See, e.g., Westergaard, *op. cit.*, chs. 13, 16.

235. Representative of the graphic matter occasionally presented are C. Babbage's charts (not printed because too large for engraving) describing the behavior of clearing-house data (XIX [1856], 28); E. Seyd's colored charts, comparing the positions of central banks (XLI [1878], 40); R. Price Williams' colored charts relating to effects of telegraph-rate reduction (XLV [1881], 12). J. T. Danson, who sometimes associated price and bank-rate changes in charts (*Economic and Statistical Studies, 1840–1890*, London, 1906), did not include these in his papers in the *JRSS*.

236. See Westergaard, *op. cit.*, pp. 148–153, 229 ff., 261 ff. In notes 13, 26 and 27, current views regarding the content and role of statistics were indicated. More or less similar views were expressed in various other numbers of the *JRSS* (e.g., I, 316; II, 25; XIII, 30; XXIII, 330; XXV, 502; XXXVII, 342; XLI, 573; XLIV, 31; XLVI, 461). Except for Jevons' earlier papers advocating the use of mathematical method, very few articles employing this method were published, in part because after 1890 the *Economic Journal* provided an alterna-

tive outlet. One exception was J. D. Everett's geometrical exposition of rent (*JRSS*, LXII [1899], 730).

237. There was not much on graphic method, though I. Fisher described its applicability to the measurement of monetary velocity (*JRSS*, LXXII [1909], 604).

238. On the work of the *Institut* see F. Zahn, *50 Années de l'institut international de statistique*, Munich, 1934.

239. Except for Falkner's translation of Meitzen's work, referred to earlier, and a translation of Walras' geometrical theory of price (III [1892–93] 45 ff.), the *Annals* of the American Academy of Political and Social Science carried no really technical paper.

240. This article, by W. Lexis, reflects the author's statistical view of economic life. He concludes that, since a multiplicity of independent, individual acts might give rise to surplus value, resort to a Marxian type of explanation was unnecessary.

241. This paper may be compared with W. M. Pearson's "Statistics and Economic Theory" (1925), reprinted in *Forecasting Business Cycles*, ch. 16.

242. As Edgeworth's many papers in the *Economic Journal* are included in his *Papers*, they are not referred to further here. Edgeworth also contributed several articles to the *Giornale* and the *Revue*.

NOTES ON CONTRIBUTORS

JOHN G. KEMENY, born in Budapest, Hungary, in 1926, received the degrees of B.A. and Ph.D. at Princeton University, where for a year he was assistant to Albert Einstein at the Institute for Advanced Study. Since 1954 he has taught mathematics at Dartmouth College. He has been consultant to the Rand Corporation on the use of high-speed computers and the construction of stochastic models, and, as Director of the Dartmouth Mathematics Project, has engaged in the application of mathematics to the social sciences. He has been Chairman of the United States Commission on Mathematical Instruction. Besides numerous articles and texts, his publications include *Introduction to Finite Mathematics; A Philosopher Looks at Science; Finite Mathematical Structures;* and *Finite Markov Chains* (the first and the last two in collaboration with others).

HAROLD D. LASSWELL, born in Donnellson, Illinois, in 1902, is Professor of Law and Political Science at the Yale University Law School. He received the degrees of Ph.B. and Ph. D. at the University of Chicago, then studied at the universities of London, Geneva, Paris, and Berlin. From 1923 to 1938 he taught at the University of Chicago, then came to Yale. From 1939 to 1945 he was Director of the War Communications Research Project at the Library of Congress, and he has been a consultant of various government departments and private organizations, as well as president of the American Political Science Association. His extensive publications include *World Politics and Personal Insecurity; Politics: Who Gets What, When, How; Power and Personality;* and, most recently, *The Policy Sciences: Recent Developments in Scope and Method* (with Daniel Lerner).

WASSILY LEONTIEF was born in 1906 in St. Petersburg (now Leningrad), Russia, where he was graduated from the University of Leningrad. His doctoral degree was conferred by the University of Berlin in 1928. After conducting research at the University of Kiel, he came to the National Bureau of Economic Research in New York, and then in 1931 to Harvard University, where he is now Henry Lee Professor of Economics, Senior Fellow of the Society of Fellows, and Director of the Economic Research Project. His work lies primarily in the field of economic theory and its application to the empirical analysis of the structure of national economies and their development. He has contributed numerous articles to American and foreign journals, and is the author of *The Structure of American Economy* and *Studies in the Structure of the American Economy.*

DANIEL LERNER, born in New York City in 1917, is Professor of Sociology and International Communication at the Massachusetts Institute of Technology, and a Senior Research Associate of its Center for International Studies. During World War II he served as Chief Editor of the intelligence branch of the Psychological Warfare Division, SHAEF, and as Chief of Intelligence in the Information Control Division of the Office of Military Government, U.S.A. His books include *Sykewar; Propaganda in War and Crisis; The Nazi Elite; France Defeats EDC* (with Raymond Aron), and *The Passing of Traditional Society.*

WALTER A. ROSENBLITH was born in Vienna, Austria, in 1913, received most of his formal education in France, and is now Professor of Communications Biophysics in M.I.T.'s Department of Electrical Engineering. Between 1939 and 1947 he was on the staff of several physics departments (New York University, University of California at Los Angeles, and the South Dakota School of Mines); from 1947 to 1951 he was a research fellow at the Harvard Psycho-Acoustic Laboratory. Since 1951, when he joined the Massachusetts Institute of Technology, he has tried, with the aid of electronic devices and mathematical models, to study neuroelectric activity in relation to the sensory performance of organisms. He is the editor of the forthcoming Symposium Volume, *Sensory Communication.*

JOSEPH J. SPENGLER, born in Piqua, Ohio, in 1902, is James B. Duke Professor of Economics at Duke University and also Director of Graduate Studies in Economics. He has taught at the University of Chicago, the University of North Carolina, Kyoto University, Ohio State University, and the University of Arizona. He has written extensively in the fields of population, economic growth, and economic and social theory. His publications include *Demographic Analysis* and *Population Theory and Policy* (both edited together with Otis Dudley Duncan).

S. S. STEVENS, born in Ogden, Utah, in 1906, is Professor of Psychology at Harvard University, and Director of the Psycho-Acoustic Laboratory, an institution devoted to research in hearing and communications. His wide interests include such areas as the philosophy of science, but he has devoted most of his professional efforts to the field of psychophysics. His undergraduate work was done at the University of Utah and Stanford University, and his doctoral degree was conferred by Harvard University in 1833. During the Second World War he served on the National Defense Research Committee, and since then as Chairman of the National Research Council, Division of Anthropology and Psychology. He is the author of *Hearing: Its Psychology and Physiology* (with Hallowell Davis); *The Varieties of Human Physique* (with W. H. Sheldon and W. B. Tucker); and *The Varieties of Temperament* (with W. H. Sheldon). He is editor of *The Handbook of Experimental Psychology.*

VICTOR F. WEISSKOPF, born in Vienna, Austria, in 1908, received his doctoral degree from the University of Göttingen in 1931. From then until 1937 he was research associate at the University of Copenhagen and at the Institute of Technology in Zurich. In 1937 he joined the faculty of the University of Rochester, and later the Manhattan Project at Los Alamos. Since 1946 he has been Professor of Physics at the Massachusetts Institute of Technology, and currently is Vice President of the American Physical Society. He has published (with John M. Blatt) a volume entitled *Theoretical Nuclear Physics,* besides his numerous articles in that field.

Guide to Further Readings

THIS LIST of readings is a highly selective guide through the extensive literature bearing on problems of quality and quantity in the fields covered by the preceding chapters. Further guidance through the literature will be found in the books listed here. Although the contributors have been most cooperative in selecting titles, responsibility for the list rests with the editor. The list follows the order of chapters in the text.

INTRODUCTION:

ON QUANTITY AND QUALITY

The great general histories of science—notably those by W. C. Dampier, C. H. Haskins, George Sarton, Charles Singer, Lynn Thorndike—interweave the issues of quantity and quality in their account of scientific development. So, in terms more narrowly related to the issues discussed in several of these papers, do the historians of mathematics—for example, W. W. R. Ball, E. T. Bell, D. E. Smith, Florian Cajori. (It is noteworthy that these problems are barely mentioned in standard histories of thought in the modern centuries—for example, those of H. O. Taylor, Leslie Stephen, Charles Merz.)

A popular and lively account, which can be appreciated for its enthusiasm rather than its historical accuracy, is Tobias Dantzig, *Number: The Language of Science,* New York: Macmillan (1930). Among the rewarding curiosa of the nontechnical literature is C. J. Keyser, *Mathematics as a Culture Clue* (1947).

An absorbing historical account of the part-whole issue, in physical science, as related to successive formulations of the infinite continuum *versus* the finite discretum, is Alaxander Koyré, *From the*

Closed World to the Infinite Universe, Baltimore: Johns Hopkins Press (1957). Social scientists will find valuable contributions to several issues discussed here—under such terms as classification, index formation, multivariate analysis, factor and scale analysis—in the two readers edited by a participant in the Hayden Colloquium on *Evidence and Inference,* P. F. Lazarsfeld: *Mathematical Thinking in the Social Sciences,* Glencoe: The Free Press (1954), and *The Language of Social Research,* Glencoe: The Free Press (1955).

IN MATHEMATICS

Arrow, K. J. *Social Choice and Individual Values,* New York: Wiley, 1951. The book discusses the problem of how society can arrive at a joint choice based on individual preferences. Much of the book relates to Model 4.

Cartwright, D. and Harary, F. "Structural Balance: A Generalization of Heider's Theory," *Psychol. Rev.* 1956, *5*:277–293. A readable article that contains a complete description of Model 1.

Kemeny, J. G., Snell, J. L., and Thompson, G. L. *Introduction to Finite Mathematics,* Englewood Cliffs, N.J.: Prentice-Hall, 1957. An elementary text on modern mathematics, with numerous applications to the social sciences. Models 2 and 3 are discussed in Chapter VII.

Kemeny, J. G. and Snell, J. L. *Mathematical Models in the Social Sciences,* Boston: Ginn, forthcoming. A series of mathematical models in the social sciences is discussed from the view of the mathematician and of the scientist. Model 4 is treated in considerable detail.

Kemeny, J. G. "Generalized Random Variables," *Pacif. J.,* forthcoming. A technical paper, treating the problem of how statistical procedures can be developed for nonnumerical data, such as in Model 4.

Luce, R. D. and Perry, A. D. "A Method of Matrix Analysis of Group Structure," *Psychometrika,* 1949, *14*:95–116. Discussion of a model closely related to Model 3.

The most important type of model falling within the realm of this article, but not treated by it, is given by the theory of games. There are many readable and elementary accounts of this important new branch of mathematics—for example, those by MacDonald, Williams, and Morgenstern.

Luce, R. D. and Raiffa, H. *Games and Decisions,* New York: Wiley, 1957. A description of recent developments and of many difficulties in the theory of games, with special attention to the problem of decision-making under uncertainty.

MacDonald, J. *Strategy in Poker, Business, and War,* New York: Norton, 1950.

Morgenstern, O. "The Theory of Games," *Sci. Amer.,* 1950, *180*:294–308.

Shapley, L. S. and Shubik, M. "A Method for Evaluating the Distribution of Power in a Committee System," *Amer. pol. Sci. Rev.,* 1954, *48*:787–792. A very interesting model for measuring voting power, somewhat in the spirit of Model 4.

Von Neumann, J. and Morgenstern, O. *Theory of Games and Economic Behavior,* Princeton: Princeton University Press, 1944. The classical treatise to which both the theory of games and many of its applications owe their start.

Williams, J. D. *The Compleat Strategyst,* New York: McGraw-Hill, 1950.

IN QUANTUM PHYSICS

Born, Max. *Restless Universe* (2d ed. rev.), New York: Dover, 1951.

Born, Max. *Natural Philosophy of Cause and Chance,* Oxford, Clarendon Press, 1948.

Born, Max. *Atomic Physics* (6th ed.), New York: Hafner, 1957.

Heisenberg, W. *Physics and Philosophy,* New York: Harper, 1958.

IN PSYCHOPHYSICS

Churchman, C. W. and Ratoosh, P. (eds.) *Measurement: Definitions and Theories,* New York: Wiley, 1959. Thirteen chapters by assorted authors, all concerned with one or another aspect of measurement and quantification. Subject matter ranges from physics to economics. Closely related to the present paper is a chapter entitled "Measurement, Psychophysics, and Utility."

Luce, R. D. "On the Possible Psychophysical Laws," *Psychol. Rev.,* 1959, *66*:81–95.

Senders, V. L. *Measurement and Statistics,* Oxford, New York: 1958. A basic text on statistical procedures, which presents the concepts of statistics within the framework of measurement theory. This is a new approach, but one that has fundamental merit.

Stevens, S. S. (ed.) *Handbook of Experimental Psychology,* New York: Wiley, 1951. The first chapter expands on some of the ideas presented here. The remainder of the book provides a systematic survey of experimental psychology, by numerous authors.

Torgerson, W. S. *Theory and Methods of Scaling,* New York: Wiley, 1958. This is the most recent and the most comprehensive treatise on the theories and methods of measuring psychological attributes. The emphasis is more on procedures than on substantive discoveries.

IN NEUROPHYSIOLOGY

BRAZIER, M. A. B. *The Electrical Activity of the Nervous System,* New York: Macmillan, 1953.

BROADBENT, D. E. *Perception and Communication,* New York: Pergamon Press, 1958.

FIELD, J. (ed.). *Handbook of Physiology,* Sec. 1: Neurophysiology. Washington, D.C.: American Physiological Society, 1959. Vol. I.

HARLOW, H. F. and WOOLSEY, C. N. (eds.). *Biological and Biochemical Bases of Behavior,* Madison: The University of Wisconsin Press, 1958.

VON NEUMANN, J. *The Computer and the Brain,* New Haven: Yale University Press, 1958.

IN POLITICS

LASSWELL, HAROLD D. *World Politics and Personal Insecurity,* New York: McGraw-Hill, 1935. See especially Chapter 1, "The Configurative Method."

LEITES, NATHAN. *A Study of Bolshevism,* Glencoe: The Free Press, 1953. Develops the "Operational Code," showing how Bolshevik elites formulate strategic principles.

LOSSKY, N. O. *History of Russian Philosophy,* New York: International Universities Press, 1951. By a former professor of philosophy, University of St. Petersburg; later, Russian Orthodox Seminary, New York. See Chapter 24.

MCDOUGAL, M. S. and associates. *Studies in World Public Order,* New Haven: Yale University Press, 1960. Programmatic papers and studies exemplifying the policy-oriented approach in jurisprudence and, especially, international law.

POOL, ITHIEL (ed.). *Trends in Content Analysis,* Urbana: University of Illinois Press, 1959. Papers and discussion at a conference of The Committee on Linguistics and Psychology, Social Science Research Council.

SCHUBERT, GLENDON A. *Quantitative Analysis of Judicial Behavior,* Glencoe: The Free Press, 1959. A recent attempt to apply quantity decisions of a type seldom dealt with in such terms.

WETTER, GUSTAVO A. *Dialectical Materialism: A Historical and Systematic Survey of Philosophy in the Soviet Union,* New York: Praeger, 1958/1959. See Part II, Chapter 3, sec. 2: "The Law of the Transition from Quantity to Quality."

IN ECONOMICS

The present state of discussion on problems of quantity and quality in economics is well represented by the following:

KOOPMANS, TJALLING C. *Three Essays on the State of Economic Science,* New York: McGraw-Hill, 1957.

STONE, RICHARD. *The Role of Measurement in Economics,* Cambridge, England: University Press, 1951.

Important historical aspects of these problems are treated in the following:

FISHER, IRVING. *The Making of Index Numbers,* Boston: Houghton Mifflin, 1922.

HUTCHISON, T. W. *A Review of Economic Doctrines, 1870–1929,* Oxford, 1953.

ROBBINS, LIONEL. *The Theory of Economic Policy,* London: Macmillan, 1952.

SCHUMPETER, JOSEPH. *The History of Economic Analysis,* New York: Oxford, 1955.

STIGLER, GEORGE J. *Production and Distribution Theories,* New York: Macmillan, 1941.

Further guidance to the literature is given in the notes to the chapter by J. J. Spengler.